Grammar Works
For Better Writing

Student's Edition

Book F

Perfection Learning®

PUBLISHER

Perfection Learning® Corporation

Editorial Director Julie A. Schumacher
Senior Editor Michael McGhee
Art Director Randy Messer

CONCEPTUALIZATION AND PRODUCTION

Victory Productions, Inc.

55 Linden Street, Worcester, MA 01609

Tel 1-508-755-0051   Fax 1-508-755-0025

Editorial Director Robert Runck
Series Coordinators George Anne Gregory, PhD, Tanya Bibeau, Alexandra Hopkins
Copy Editors Sherry Pitler, Sara Kras, Cynthia Adler, Talbot F. Hamlin, Pamela M. Banks
Art Director Victoria Porras
Design Victoria Porras, Paul Leone, Raúl E. Payva
Cover Design Ana E. Cordero
Illustrator John Kastner
Production Director Kimberly Medvezcky

What Is Grammar Anyway?

We use grammar when we talk and write. By using grammar, we can put our sentences and words into an order that helps us to speak and write clearly. Here is an example.

Hello students. How are you?

Using grammar when we speak or write allows others to understand us. Without grammar, people might speak or write in many different ways. It would be difficult for others to understand. Here is an example.

students hello how you are

If we think about this group of words long enough, we can understand that somebody is saying hello and asking how we are. But, it would have been much easier if the writer had followed grammar rules.

How To Use This Book

This workbook will teach you grammar rules. The rules will help you write better.

This workbook will give you examples of how different grammar rules are used. It will explain what the rule means.

There are five steps to each lesson.

- In the **Learn It** section, you learn the rule.
- In the **Find It** section, you see how the rule has been used.
- In the **Try It** section, you write something that uses the rule.
- In the **Fix It** section, you make writing better by using the rule.
- In the **Review It** section, you review what you have learned.

After a few lessons, you will practice using the rules that you have learned.

Have an enjoyable time learning how to use grammar in your writing.

Table of Contents

Unit 3 Predicate Nouns and Predicate Adjectives

Unit 4 Phrases

Unit 5 Verb Tenses

Student Handbook

Lesson 1

Paragraphs

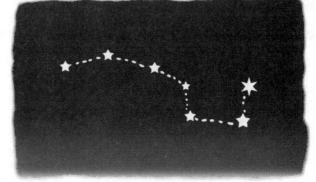

A paragraph contains a main idea
and supporting details.

1. Read this.

> <u>A look into the night sky on a clear night can be really exciting!</u> There are
> many constellations, or star groups, to see. One constellation is Ursa Major, which
> is Latin for "Great Bear." Seven stars in the Great Bear form the "Big Dipper." If
> you make a line using the two stars in the cup of the dipper, you will find Polaris,
> the North Star.

**This is a paragraph. It contains a main idea, or topic sentence, that tells what the paragraph
is about. The main idea is underlined.**

**A paragraph also has several details that tell you more about the main idea. The sentences
about Ursa Major are details.**

2. Place checkmarks next to two other details in the paragraph.

**The beginning of paragraphs is usually indented, or set in from the margin. An indent lets
readers know that a new idea is going to be introduced.**

1. Read the paragraph below. Put a check on the indent.

> People have been observing the stars since before historic times. Ancient
> sailors used them to guide them across oceans. Ptolemy, an ancient Greek, listed 48
> constellations. Much of what we learn today comes from his observations. Of
> course, all people, including Africans, Asians, Australians, and Americans, had their
> own names for the constellations. While Europeans, Asians, and North Americans
> observed the constellations in the northern sky, Africans, Australians, and South
> Americans observed different constellations in the southern sky.

2. How many sentences does it have? _____

3. Underline the topic sentence of this paragraph.

1. Write a paragraph about what you can see in the sky. Put a check on the indent.

_____

_____

_____

_____

_____

2. Write the letters *MI* next to the main idea. _____

3. Write the letter *D* next to each detail. _____

_____

_____

Fix It

Read this paragraph. Then follow the directions.

What do Inuits, Plains Indians, ancient sailors, and American slaves have in common? They used the North Star to help them find their way. Inuits used the North Star to travel across the frozen, treeless land, especially in winter when the sun barely shows. Plains Indians used that same star to travel across the vast prairies of the Great Plains. Ancient sailors looked for the North Star since no land indicated to them where they were. American slaves also relied on the North Star, which they called the "Drinking Gourd." Those escaping slavery traveled on the Underground Railroad to the North. Because they moved at night, the North Star helped guide them.

1. What is missing from this paragraph? _____

2. Circle the main idea.

3. Write two supporting details from the paragraph.

_____

_____

Lesson 2

Quotation Marks

Quotation marks enclose the exact words of a speaker.

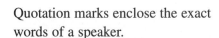

Read this.

> My friend Gibrón Aviña says, "Panama City is the most beautiful place in the world."

> "More beautiful than my hometown, Eureka Springs, Arkansas?" I laugh.

> He looks at me seriously with his black eyes. "Yes, I believe so," he replies.

A. We use quotation marks when we write what someone says. Use a comma to introduce the quote when the quote begins in the middle of a sentence.

Find a sentence in the paragraph above that introduces a quote with a comma and write the sentence on the line below.

_____

B. Use a comma to mark the end of a quoted sentence when it is followed by words that tell who is speaking.

Find a sentence in the paragraph above that contains this and write it on the line below.

_____

Put the letter of the punctuation rule used in each of these sentences.

Eddie said, "What year was the Panama Canal built?" _____

"It was built between 1901 and 1914," Mike replied. _____

"Let's see what our history book says," Susanne suggested. _____

"That sounds like a good idea," Mike answered. _____

Write a sentence using each rule from "Learn It."

_____

_____

_____

_____

_____

_____

Fix It

These sentences are missing punctuation. Rewrite them using the correct punctuation.

Sam asked Does anyone know anything about Panama

Yeah, I do Georgia replied. What do you want to know

I'm doing a report for my social studies class Sam said.

Great! Would you like some help? Georgia smiled.

Sam smiled Sure when can we begin?

_____

_____

_____

_____

_____

_____

_____

_____

Lesson 3

More Quotation Marks

Punctuating quotations can be tricky.

 **Learn It**

1. Read this.

   "Hey," Eduardo said, "what do want to do when you grow up?"

   Use a pair of commas when the person speaking interrupts what is said. Put the first comma inside the quotation marks. Use the second one to introduce the rest of the quote. Do not start the second part of the interrupted quote with a capital letter.

2. Circle the two commas in the sentence above.

3. Read this.

   Marita said, "I want to be a cartoonist!"

   Did Marita really say, "I want to be a cartoonist"?

   An exclamation mark or question mark is placed *inside* quotation marks when it punctuates the quotation. It is placed *outside* quotation marks when it punctuates the main sentence.

 **Find It**

1. Underline the words that interrupt the quotes in this dialog.

   "Look," Ginny said, "there's a job fair at school. Let's go!"

   "No," Samantha said, "I'm not looking for a job just yet."

2. Correctly add question marks or exclamation marks to these sentences.

   I shouted, " That was great "

   Did you say, "I want to be a baseball player"

   I can't believe Vonnell said, "Athletes are overpaid"

Write a conversation between two people. Use interrupted quotes, question marks, and exclamation points.

_____

_____

_____

_____

_____

_____

_____

_____

_____

_____

_____

Add any missing punctuation to these sentences.

"Man Gabe begins "There sure are enough booths here.

Yeah, I don't even know where to begin, Abby replies. Let's go talk to those people at the Internet booth.

"OK Gabe answers.

Hello, can I help you? Ms. Jones asks. Are you interested in helping people get onto the Internet?

Sure we say excitedly.

Good, Ms. Jones smiles warmly.

What do you know about computers   she asks.

Extra Practice

Lesson 1

Lesson 2

Lesson 3

It is time to practice what you have learned. You have learned about paragraphs, quotation marks, interrupted quotes, and the correct use of punctuation with quotation marks.

1. What does the topic sentence in a paragraph tell? _____

_____

2. Think of a topic for a paragraph and write a topic sentence on the blank lines below.

_____

_____

3. Write a short paragraph using the topic sentence you just wrote. Be sure to include details.

_____

_____

_____

_____

_____

_____

_____

_____

_____

4. Write two sentences that use commas to introduce quotes.

_____

_____

_____

_____

5. Write two sentences with interrupted quotes.

_____

_____

_____

_____

6. Write two sentences that show the speakers first and their quoted statements last.

_____

_____

_____

_____

7. Write two sentences that show the speakers asking a question.

_____

_____

_____

_____

8. Write two sentences that show the speakers using strong emotion.

_____

_____

_____

_____

Name _____ Date _____ Class _____

 Lesson 4

Coordinating Conjunctions

You can use a comma and a coordinating conjunction to join sentences.

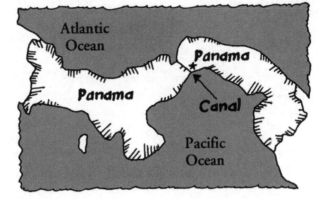

Learn It

1. Read these sentences.

   Ships travel on oceans. They travel on other waterways.

   Ships travel on oceans, or they travel on other waterways.

   Remember when you put two complete sentences together with a coordinating conjunction, use a comma at the end of the first sentence and before the coordinating conjunction. Coordinating conjunctions include *and, but, or, nor, for, so,* **and** *yet.*

2. Read this sentence.

   The United States built the Panama Canal, but ships from all countries use it.

3. What are the complete sentences?

   _____   _____

Find It

1. Underline the sentences that use a coordinating conjunction to join two complete sentences.

   The Atlantic Ocean and the Pacific Ocean border Central America.

   The United States wanted to build a canal there, but the swampy land was an obstacle.

   A narrow strip of land is an isthmus.

   The workers encountered many hardships, but the canal was finished in 1914.

2. Write the two complete sentences that were joined into one.

   _____   _____

   _____   _____

Write three sentences using coordinating conjunctions and commas between complete sentences.

_____

_____

_____

_____

_____

_____

Fix It

1. Use a coordinating conjunction and a comma to make a compound sentence out of each pair of sentences below.

   There is an isthmus in the country of Panama. It connects Central and South America.

   _____ _____

   _____

   _____

   The land belonged to Colombia. Colombia didn't want a canal.

   _____

   _____

   The United States had to give up its idea. The United States had to look for a way around the obstacles.

   _____

   _____

   _____

2. Write the coordinating conjunctions that you used in your sentences from number 1 on the blank lines below.

   _____   _____   _____

Lesson 5

Interjections

Interjections show emotion or strong feeling.

Learn It

1. Read these sentences.

Ugh! Our best player has been sidelined with an injury.

Ouch! My foot got stepped on in the crowded stadium.

Our quarterback has fumbled the ball. Oh no!

Interjections are words or phrases used to show emotion. Interjections start with capital letters and usually end with exclamation points.

2. Read this sentence.

Oh, I thought you were at the store.

When an interjection does not show strong emotion, it is punctuated with a comma.

Find It

Circle the interjections in the following sentences.

Our team will be hard to beat tonight. Yeah!

Yikes! The quarterback is about to get sacked.

He got the ball off. Oh, just in time.

Hey! The ball is on the three-yard line.

Oops, he dropped the ball.

Phew, I thought the test was today.

Oh, the test is tomorrow.

The book is at home Great!

Oh! Jenny has a book.

1. Write a note to a friend describing something you enjoyed. It can be a sporting event, a television show, a movie, or an actual event. Use at least three interjections.

_____

_____

_____

_____

2. Think of something you feel strongly about and write a short letter to the newspaper. Use some interjections. Be sure to punctuate correctly.

_____

_____

_____

_____

_____

Fix It

Read the following description of the last part of a football game. Then add the interjections Hurray! and Amazing!

There are 37 seconds left on the clock. The Cougars are four points behind. The quarterback pretends to hand the ball off, but he keeps it. He plows through the defensive line and goes over for the touchdown. This is the first win for the Cougars this season.

_____

_____

_____

_____

Lesson 6

Interjections and Sentences

Use a comma or an exclamation point to punctuate an interjection.

Learn It

Read these sentences.

"Virgil (Gus) Grissom was one of the first U.S. astronauts," Mrs. Kilham said.

"He was not chosen to make the first U.S. space flight. Oh, how disappointing," she continued.

Use interjections to show the emotions or attitude of the speaker. Quotation marks show someone is speaking. They are used to show what a person said or how he or she said it.

Punctuate a sentence that has an interjection with a comma or an exclamation point, depending on how strong the emotion is.

Find It

Circle any interjections in the following sentences.

"Luckily, Gus Grissom was chosen to be the second U.S. astronaut in space." Mrs. Kilham told the class.

"Who knows what happened on that flight?" she asked.

"Oh! I know Mrs. Kilham," Jimmy answered excitedly.

"Blast off, re-entry, and splashdown went as planned," he said. "Then, disaster! The space capsule's hatch blew open, and it began to fill with water," he concluded.

Mrs. Kilham said. "Great! That is right, Jimmy. Did you also know that Grissom was able to escape the capsule and keep afloat until a helicopter rescued him?" she asked.

"Oh, I didn't," he answered.

"Years later, they even found the capsule," she concluded.

Write a paragraph about an event. It can be real or make-believe. Use interjections and quotes.

_____

_____

_____

_____

_____

Fix It

The following dialog is missing quotation marks and interjections. Rewrite the dialog on the blank lines so that it includes both. Choose interjections from the box.

Oh!	Excellent,	Oh,	Excellent!

Gus Grissom remained an astronaut and worked to help put a man on the moon, Mrs. Kilham told the class. Who knows how he died? she asked.

Mrs. Kilham, I know! Jenny said excitedly.

He was performing a test with two other astronauts inside a space capsule filled with pure oxygen. A spark caused a fire and all three died, she said.

Their work, however, still helped to get two men to the moon, Mrs. Kilham responded.

_____

_____

_____

_____

_____

_____

_____

Name _____ Date _____ Class _____

Extra Practice

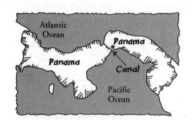

Lesson 4

Lesson 5

Lesson 6

It is time to practice what you have learned. You have learned about compound sentences, coordinating conjunctions, interjections, and quotation marks.

1. Combine these sentences and use the conjunction suggested.

My dad and I used to go fishing. My mom did not. (but)

_____

_____

My dad and I fished for catfish. We fished for bass. (and)

_____

_____

I liked to fish with my dad. I didn't like to get up early. (but)

_____

_____

My mom made breakfast. She packed a lunch. (and)

_____

_____

My dad put everything in the old Studebaker. He put me in the front seat. (and)

_____

_____

2. Write a composition using interjections. Punctuate the composition correctly.

_____

_____

_____

_____

_____

_____

_____

_____

3. Write a dialog between two people. Include interjections and quotation marks.

_____

_____

_____

_____

_____

_____

_____

_____

_____

_____

_____

Name _____   Date _____   Class _____

Lesson 7
Compound Subjects

A sentence may have more than one subject.

1. Read these sentences.

    Ursa Major is a constellation. Orion is a constellation.

    Betelgeuse is a star in Orion. Rigel is a star in Orion.

    The subject of a sentence is a word or group of words that is doing something or about which something is said. The subject in each of the above sentences is underlined.

2. Read these sentences.

    Ursa Major and Orion are constellations.

    Betelgeuse and Rigel are stars in Orion.

    Two or more subjects joined by a coordinating conjunction make a compound subject. Notice that the verb was changed to agree with the new plural subject. Most compound subjects require a plural verb.

3. Read this sentence.

    Ursa Major, Ursa Minor, and Orion are constellations.

    When combining three or more subjects use commas between the subjects.

Circle the compound subjects in the following paragraph.

    Planets, satellites, and asteroids travel through the night sky. Mercury and Venus can be seen clearly because they are closest to earth. Polaris is at the end of the Big Dipper. Sailors and explorers have used the North Star for navigation. Unfortunately, both rain and clouds sometimes hide the North Star.

1. Write a sentence with two subjects to create a compound subject.

_____

_____

2. Write a sentence with at least three subjects to create a compound subject.

_____

_____

3. Write a paragraph about the objects that you see in the sky. Include at least three compound subjects.

_____

_____

_____

_____

_____

Fix It

Use compound subjects to rewrite this paragraph. Be sure verbs agree with compound subjects.

Venus is visible from Earth. Mars is visible from Earth also. Bright lights make it hard to see the stars. Clouds make it hard to see the stars. People who live in the Northern Hemisphere see different constellations than people who live in the Southern Hemisphere. Australians see different constellations than we do. New Zealanders see different constellations than we do. Africans see different constellations than we do.

_____

_____

_____

_____

Lesson 8

Predicates

Every sentence has a subject and predicate.

1. Read these sentences.

The Inuit people *live in Canada, Alaska, and Greenland.*

Some *build winter homes out of snow.*

These winter homes *are called igloos.*

Igloo *is an Inuit word that means shelter.*

Inuits *have kayaks and snowshoes.*

A sentence has a subject and a predicate. In most sentences, the simple predicate follows the subject and tells what the subject does, has, is, or has done to it. The complete predicate always has a verb as a part of it. In each of the above sentences, the complete predicate has been italicized.

2. Read these sentences.

The Inuits *once* hunted whales.

Sometimes the complete predicate begins with an adverb.

3. *Do* you *think they still hunt whales*?

In some interrogative sentences, part of the verb is split.

1. Read the following sentences and underline the complete predicates.

Do you think the Inuits still make kayaks?

I wonder what Inuits live in during the summer.

Igloos are built out of ice.

2. Circle the sentence that starts with a verb.

1. Write a sentence and underline the predicate.

_____

_____

2. Write a sentence that begins the predicate with an adverb.

_____

_____

3. Write an interrogative sentence that has part of the verb split.

_____

_____

Fix It

These predicates have not been correctly identified. Write the sentences and underline the complete predicate in each sentence.

Inuits are Eskimos <u>living in Alaska</u>.

Do igloos <u>melt quickly in the spring</u>.

Snowshoes and kayaks are means of transportation <u>for the Eskimos</u>.

<u>Have</u> you ever met an Inuit?

_____

_____

_____

_____

_____

_____

_____

Lesson 9
Verbals

A verbal is a verb used as a noun or an adjective.

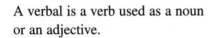

1. Read this paragraph.

> The winds blow across the *changing* sand dunes of the Kalahari Desert. These *whirling* winds catch the loose sand and toss it carelessly into the *heated* air. *Scurrying* rodents make crazy patterns in the sand. *Running* rapidly is the only way to avoid *being* scorched by the heat.

Verbs can be used in different ways. One form of a verb can tell what a subject in a sentence does or is. Another form of a verb can be used as an adjective or as a noun.

2. Write *run* on this blank line: _____ Change run to *running*: _____

The -ing form of a verb is called a *present participle*. A present participle can be used as a noun or as an adjective.

3. Read these sentences.

Running is the only way to avoid the heat.   *Running* water has a gentle sound.

In the first sentence, the present particple *running* is used as a *noun*. *Running* is the subject in the sentence. In the second sentence, the present participle *running* is used as an *adjective*. *Running* tells what *kind* of water has a gentle sound.

4. Now read this sentence.

The *exhausted* campers fell asleep next to the stream.

The -ed form of a verb is called a *past participle*. A past participle can be used as an adjective. In this sentence, the past participle *exhausted* describes the campers.

Underline the verbals in these sentences.

As we lay in our sleeping bags, a loud, screeching owl woke us.

Sometime shortly before dawn, we awake to the howling coyote.

Write five sentences using present and past participles as adjectives and nouns.

_____

_____

_____

_____

_____

_____

_____

_____

_____

• •

Change the underlined verbs into participles. Write the participle above the line.

The <u>hunt</u> coatimundi eats berries.

Have you ever heard of the <u>blaze</u> Sonoran Desert?

You might encounter <u>dig</u> skunk looking for grubs.

If you are lucky, you might see the almost extinct bobcat <u>lurk</u> among rocks or brushy thickets.

You will probably see a tumbleweed go <u>roll</u> by.

You can only see these exotic animals if you leave the comfort of your home and go <u>camp</u> in the remoteness of the Southwest.

The only relief from the heat comes with the <u>set</u> sun.

Extra Practice

Lesson 7   **Lesson 8**   **Lesson 9**

It is time to practice what you have learned. You have learned about compound subjects, predicates, and verbals.

1. Write a sentence with a compound subject.

_____

_____

2. Write a sentence with three subjects.

_____

_____

3. Write a sentence with a predicate.

_____

_____

4. Write a sentence with a complete predicate that begins with an adverb.

_____

_____

5. Write an interrogative sentence with a predicate that has a part of the verb split.

_____

_____

6. Underline the complete predicate in each of the sentences above.

7. Write a sentence with a present participle used as a noun.

_____

_____

8. Write a sentence with a present participle used as an adjective.

_____

_____

9. Write a sentence with a past participle used as an adjective.

_____

_____

10. Write a paragraph that has participles used as nouns and adjectives in at least two sentences.

_____

_____

_____

_____

_____

_____

_____

_____

_____

_____

Lesson 10

Review

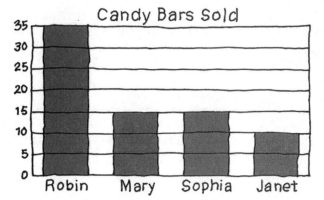

Candy Bars Sold

Review It ♩

1. Fill in the blanks with the right answer.

A paragraph contains one _____. Other sentences containing

_____ tell more about the main idea.

A _____ is a word that puts two sentences together.

We use a(n) _____ before the coordinating conjunction when it connects two sentences.

Use a(n) _____ when an interjection shows strong emotion.

Use a(n) _____ when an interjection does *not* show strong emotion.

A compound subject is two or more subjects connected by a _____.

A predicate completes the sentence and gives further information about the

_____. It contains a verb that tells what the subject does, has, is, or what is done to it.

To show the exact words someone says, use _____.

2. Name the part of the following sentences that is underlined.

Mean, median, and mode are math terms. _____

The Cougar cheerleaders want to go to the tournament, so they made money selling candy bars.

_____

Wow! Robin sold 35 bars. _____

Mary and Sophia sold 15 bars each, and Janet sold 10 bars. _____

Robin sold 12 boxes. _____

Robin always sells a lot! _____

3. Write a short paragraph on a topic that you find interesting. Be sure to punctuate sentences correctly and to combine sentences when you can.

_____

_____

_____

_____

4. Combine sentences and use correct punctuation to rewrite the following paragraph.

      July and August are the hottest months. This year July was hot. This year August was cold and rainy. Unfortunately, we took a five-day vacation in August. The high temperatures for each day were 65 degrees, 72 degrees, 59 degrees, 60 degrees, and 55 degrees. Oh misery.

_____

_____

_____

_____

5. Write a sentence with a verbal noun.

_____

_____

6. Write a sentence with a verbal adjective.

_____

_____

Name _____ Date _____ Class _____

Lesson 1

Predicates with Transitive and Intransitive Verbs

A verb can be transitive or intransitive.

1. Read this.

subject	*transitive verb*	*direct object*
The police officer	stopped	the traffic.

The verb *stopped* is a **transitive verb.** It transfers action from the subject to the direct object *traffic.*

2. Read this sentence.

subject	*intransitive verb*	*prepositional phrase*
My uncle's car	stalled	in traffic.

The verb *stalled* is an **intransitive verb.** The action of the subject is complete without a direct object.

Remember, a sentence is a complete thought. If you say *car stalled,* you have a more or less complete thought. It doesn't matter *where* the car stalled or *when* (*in traffic, during rush hour*). An intransitive verb doesn't need an object.

If you say, however, *the police officer stopped the,* you do not have a complete thought. You need and want to know *who* or *what* was stopped. A transitive verb must have an object to complete the action.

Find It

Underline the transitive verbs. Circle the intransitive verbs.

Caution signs tell us to slow down.

Angela stopped quickly.

My dad drives fast.

A sign at a railroad crossing warns a driver.

It tells the driver to slow down, look, and listen.

Write five sentences with transitive verbs.

_____

_____

_____

_____

_____

_____

_____

_____

_____

_____

Fix It

1. Here is an article from a newspaper. Add any transitive or intransitive verbs or direct objects that are missing.

Last night, Homer Peabody _____ his _____ home. He _____

a sign. It _____ "Deer Crossing." A deer _____ the road. Homer

swerved and _____ a _____. Paramedics _____ to Homer. A tow

truck _____ his _____ away. Luckily Homer and the deer were okay.

2. List the transitive verbs you added to the above paragraph.

_____   _____   _____   _____   _____   _____

3. How many direct objects did you add to the paragraph? _____

_____

Name _____ Date _____ Class _____

Lesson 2

What Is a Direct Object?

A transitive verb has a direct object. The direct object can be a noun or pronoun.

Read these sentences.

My friend Joe owns a *restaurant*.

He serves delicious *pizzas*.

A good customer wanted *something special*.

A transitive verb carries the action from the subject to something or someone else, called a *direct object*. **The direct object can be a noun or a pronoun.**

The direct objects in these sentences are *restaurant, pizza,* and *something*.

The direct object receives the action of the transitive verb.

Find It

1. Joe's customer wanted him to make a pizza with eels on it. The customer also wanted Joe to cut the pizza into five equal parts. Read how Joe did it. Circle the direct objects in the sentences below.

   Joe got the eels.

   He chopped them into small pieces.

   He cooked the pizza.

   Joe divided the pizza into five slices.

2. Write the transitive verbs from each sentence on the blank lines below.

   _____   _____   _____   _____

Try It

Write five sentences with transitive verbs and direct objects.

_____

_____

_____

_____

_____

_____

_____

_____

_____

_____

Fix It

Complete the following sentences that tell how Joe makes pizza. Add direct objects to each.

First, Joe gets _____

Then, he measures _____

Next, he adds _____

Then, Joe shapes _____

Next, Joe sprinkles _____

Then, he pours on _____

Next, he cooks _____

Then, Joe cuts _____

Finally, he serves _____

Lesson 3

Finding the Direct Object

A direct object is always a noun or a pronoun.

1. Read these sentences.

   Joe cut the customer's special pizza into five equal parts.

   My mom makes great pizza.

   I eat pizza all the time.

   To find the direct object in a sentence, ask yourself *who* or *what* receives the action.

   Transitive verbs always have direct objects. Remember, a direct object is always a noun or a pronoun, never an adjective or adverb. The direct object in the first example is *pizza*, not *customer's* or *special*.

2. Underline the transitive verbs in the sentences above.

3. Circle the direct objects in the sentences above.

Find It

Circle the transitive verb in each of the sentences below. Then write the direct object on the blank line.

I hear the children. _____

A clever person solves many problems. _____

Jerry threw the ball. _____

Many people write books. _____

Molly broke the glass. _____

The students chose Mr. Smith. _____

1. Write four sentences with direct objects.

_____

_____

_____

_____

_____

_____

_____

2. Circle the transitive verbs in your sentences.

3. Underline the direct objects.

4. Underline the transitive verbs and circle the direct objects in the following paragraph.

> The Greek Archimedes made many contributions to math and science. We still use his theories today. His home town was attacked by Romans. At the time, Archimedes was studying a problem in geometry. He asked the Roman not to disturb him. The soldier was furious. He drew his sword. Archimedes was murdered.

Fix It

In the sentences below circle the direct objects and then write new ones. You may add adjectives and adverbs to the direct objects.

Jenny gave a speech. _____

I found a kitten. _____

I fed the baby. _____

I hid the ball. _____

Extra Practice

Lesson 1

Lesson 2

LET'S THROW DAD A PARTY!

Lesson 3

Unit 2

It is time to practice what you have learned. You have learned about transitive and intransitive verbs and direct objects.

1. Circle the sentences below that have transitive verbs.

Signs tell many things.

Railroad signs warn motorists that a train could be coming.

A stop sign warns a driver to stop.

My uncle drives slowly.

He never gets a speeding ticket.

2. Write a sentence with a transitive verb. Circle the verb.

_____

_____

3. Find the intransitive verbs in the sentences below and circle them.

Uncle Fred reads well.

Sometimes he reads aloud to me.

I enjoy listening.

He enjoys reading.

4. Write a sentence with an intransitive verb. Circle the verb.

_____

_____

5. Write a paragraph that uses both transitive and intransitive verbs.

_____

_____

_____

_____

_____

_____

6. Write four sentences with transitive verbs.

_____

_____

_____

_____

_____

_____

7. Write the direct objects from your sentences in exercises 5 and 6 on the blank lines below.

_____

_____

_____

_____

Lesson 4

Compound Direct Objects

The Himalayan Mountains

You can combine sentences by
using compound direct objects.

Learn It

1. Read these sentences.

  Last summer, Denise visited <u>China</u>.   Last summer, Denise visited <u>India</u>.

  Last summer, Denise visited <u>China and India</u>.

  Last summer Denise visited *where*? She visited *China* and *India*. China and India are the direct
  objects. They receive the action directly from the subject.

  **Direct objects can be single or compound. As with other compounds, you join the direct objects
  with a conjunction. When sentences have the same subject and verb, they can be combined to
  make one sentence with a compound direct object.**

2. What are the similar subjects and verbs in the sentences above?

  _____   _____

Find It

1. Denise is a geologist. She studies the earth and its formations. Read the sentences below and
  underline the compound direct objects.

  Denise took geology and Chinese in college.

  She studied small stones and large mountains.

  She researched the Himalayan Mountains and their formation.

  In her travels, she rode planes, trains, and even elephants.

  Last summer she also visited Tibet and Kashmir.

2. What are the transitive verbs in the sentences above?

  _____   _____   _____   _____   _____

1. Write three sentences with compound direct objects.

_____

_____

_____

_____

_____

_____

2. Write a paragraph about another country or society. It can be real or imagined. Underline the direct objects. Circle any compound direct objects.

_____

_____

_____

_____

_____

_____

_____

Fix It

Use compound direct objects to finish these sentences.

In China, Denise saw _____

The restaurants served _____

In the country, the farmers grew _____

The city was filled with _____

Unit 2

Lesson 5

What is an Indirect Object?

Many sentences contain indirect objects.

Compare these sentences.

Denise sent *her boss* a report.

She drew *him* a map.

An indirect object names a person or thing that indirectly receives the action of the verb. It comes between the verb and the direct object. It answers the question "to or for whom?"

Denise sent a report.

She drew a map.

A direct object names a person or thing that directly receives the action of the verb.

Find It

1. Look at each group of sentences below. Draw one line under the indirect object. Draw two lines under the direct object.

   Denise showed the class a fossil.

   Denise told the students her adventures.

   The students asked Denise many questions.

   Denise showed a fossil.

   Denise told her adventures.

   The students asked many questions.

2. Write the transitive verb from each sentence on the blank lines below.

   _____   _____   _____

   _____   _____   _____

3. Here is a paragraph about Denise's trip. Underline the indirect objects. Circle the direct objects.

   Denise met an old man. He gave her a fossil. Later, she sent him a

   thank-you note. Denise bought her parents presents. She sent her father a cane

   and bought her mother a silk fan.

1. Write five sentences with indirect objects.

_____

_____

_____

_____

_____

_____

_____

_____

2. Write a thank–you note for a present that you received. Draw one line under any indirect objects.

_____

_____

_____

_____

Fix It

Add indirect objects to these sentences.

Two weeks later, Denise gave _____ a speech.

She showed the _____ a marine fossil.

On her trip, Denise also bought _____ presents.

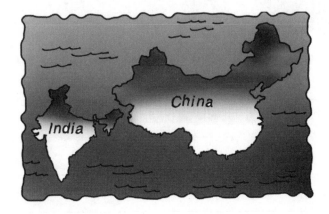

Lesson 6

Finding the Indirect Object

An indirect object answers *to whom* or *for whom* the action is being carried out.

Learn It

Read these sentences. Find the direct object in each.

Mrs. Dennis showed the class a movie.

She asked them to write a short report.

They wrote her their reports.

In the first sentence, the direct object is *movie,* not *class*. In the second sentence, the direct object is *them*. In the third sentence, the direct object is *reports,* not *her*. The words *class* and *her* in these sentences are indirect objects. To tell if a word is an indirect object, place the word *to* or *for* in front of it. If the sentence still makes sense, the word is an indirect object.

showed [to] the class a movie   wrote [for] her their reports

Find It

1. Underline the indirect objects in these sentences.

    Denise planned an Indian meal for her friends.

    She mailed them invitations.

    Denise then sent a chef in India an email.

    He gave her a special recipe.

2. On the blank lines write the transitive verbs in these sentences.

    _____   _____   _____   _____

3. Circle the direct object of each sentence in number 1 above.

4. How many of the sentences had an indirect object? _____

Try It

1. Write four sentences with indirect objects. Use the transitive verbs *told*, *played*, *sang*, and *showed*.

_____

_____

_____

_____

_____

_____

_____

_____

2. Write the indirect objects from your sentences on the blank lines below.

_____   _____   _____   _____

Fix It

1. Add indirect objects to the paragraph below.

　　　　During Denise's presentation, one boy asked _____ this question: "How

did the marine fossils get into the mountains?" She gave _____ this explanation:

"Some people believe that one landmass hit another, trapping marine animals. The

collision gave the _____ a violent shock. The landmasses rose up and formed

mountains." At the end, we gave _____ a standing ovation.

2. These sentences do not have the correct indirect objects underlined. Rewrite each sentence and underline the correct indirect object.

Please give me the <u>soup</u>.　　　　　　　　Mark gave Arthur the <u>book</u>.

_____

_____

Extra Practice

The Himalayan Mountains

Lesson 4

Lesson 5

China

India

Lesson 6

It is time to practice what you have learned. You have learned about compound direct objects and indirect objects.

1. Underline the compound direct objects in the following sentences.

  Matt collects old recipes and cookbooks.

  He cooks delicious meals and snacks.

  His meals include soups, salads, and desserts.

  People like his soups and desserts.

2. Write the transitive verbs from the sentences above on the blank lines.

  _____ _____ _____ _____

3. Write four sentences with compound direct objects.

_____

_____

_____

_____

_____

_____

_____

_____

4. Underline the indirect objects in the following sentences.

Matt's sister, Eryn, emailed her friends his tortilla soup recipe.

Matt wrote Eryn an angry email message.

Eryn gave Matt a promise that she wouldn't do this again.

She sent him an apology.

5. Write the direct objects for each of the sentences above on the blank lines below.

_____   _____   _____   _____

6. Write the transitive verbs for the sentences above on the blank lines below.

_____   _____   _____   _____

7. Rewrite the sentences. Change objects of prepositions to indirect objects.

Matt cooks dinner for Marsha.

Matt's sister Eryn had emailed the recipe to her many friends.

Eryn gave a promise to Matt that she wouldn't do this again.

She sent an apology to him.

_____

_____

_____

_____

_____

8. Write a sentence with an indirect object.

_____

_____

9. Write a sentence with a compound direct object and an indirect object.

_____

_____

10. Write the transitive verbs from numbers eight and nine on the blank line below.

_____   _____

Lesson 7

Compound Indirect Objects

Mr. Larson handed Julie and
David their diplomas.

Learn It

Read these sentences.

My mom gave *my best friend and me* tickets to a movie.

She told *my dad and my brother* that she couldn't take us.

She handed the tickets to *Rosa and me*.

A compound indirect object is two or more indirect objects joined by a conjunction. Use the object form of a pronoun (me, him, her, us, them, you, it).

Some verbs that let you use an indirect object or a compound indirect object immediately after the verb include *make, give, send, offer, show, write,* and *tell.*

Some people make a serious grammatical error when using indirect objects. They say such expressions as "gave my mom and I. . ." or "sent Bill and she. . .". Never use the nominative form of a personal pronoun in an indirect object.

Find It

1. Underline the compound indirect objects in the following sentences.

Our ESL teacher gave the class this lesson:

"José, give María and Consuelo two blue books."

"María, hand Houng and Boris their books."

"Boris, pass me one book and two pencils."

"Consuelo, pass Boris one eraser."

"Houng, give María, Boris, and José a pencil."

"Consuelo, give María and Houng a book."

2. How many sentences had compound indirect objects? _____

Write three sentences with compound indirect objects.

_____

_____

_____

_____

_____

Fix It

Combine each pair of sentences below. Underline any compound indirect objects.

The savings account pays Mark 4.5% interest. The savings account pays Julie 4.5% interest.

_____

_____

The Lees showed Julie the bank statement. The Lees showed Mark the bank statement.

_____

_____

The bank sends Mark a statement every month. The bank sends Julie a statement every month.

_____

_____

When the bank loans money, it charges people interest. When the bank loans money, it charges businesses interest.

_____

_____

Name _____   Date _____   Class _____

Unit 2

Lesson 8

Finding Direct and Indirect Objects

The direct object receives the action. The indirect object names *for whom* or *to whom* the action went.

Learn It

1. Read these sentences.

   We salute Charles Babbage.   The world owes Mr. Babbage much.

   The direct object receives the action. The indirect object names *for whom* or *to whom* the action went.

   List the direct objects in the two sentences above. _____ _____

   List the indirect objects. _____

2. Now read this sentence.

   Charles Babbage built the first mechanical device capable of processing information.

   Here, Charles Babbage is the subject. The word *built* is a transitive verb, so we know we will have a direct object. To find the direct object we ask, "What did Babbage build?"

   He built the first mechanical *device* capable of processing information.

Find It

1. Circle the direct objects and underline the indirect objects in the following sentences.

   The first computers solved mathematical equations for their users.

   Mr. and Mrs. Lee are buying Mark and Julie either a desktop computer or a notebook computer.

   They sent the IBM Corporation and the Apple Corporation letters.

   They gave their twins a powerful computer.

2. Write the transitive verb for each of these sentences on the blank lines.

   _____ _____ _____ _____

1. Write two sentences with direct and indirect objects.

   _____

   _____

   _____

   _____

2. Write a paragraph about an invention. Include transitive verbs, direct objects, and indirect objects.

   _____

   _____

   _____

   _____

   _____

Fix It

Add direct or indirect objects where needed.

The First National Bank sent _____ his statement.

Mr. Johnson read _____ and found an error in the interest.

He used his _____ to analyze it.

The computer processed the information and printed _____ out.

The computer found _____ in his statement.

Mr. Johnson wrote _____ a letter.

The bank sent _____ an apology.

They also sent him a(n) _____.

Unit 2

Lesson 9

Writing with Direct and Indirect Objects

Direct and indirect objects are vital to your writing and speaking.

Learn It

Read this.

First National Bank
100 Main Street
Anywhere, Any State 00000

March 15, 2000

Mike Johnson
521 Smith Street
Anywhere, Any State 00000

Dear Mr. Johnson:

We are writing you this letter to explain your last statement. We send you statements monthly. However, we pay interest every three months. Therefore, interest will appear on your statement only four times a year.

We can open a Super Saver Account for you. It compounds interest daily. If you are considering this account, contact Sara Cunningham. She will give you any help necessary.

Sincerely,

Reginald Jackson, President

You use indirect and direct objects in writing and in speech. This writer has used both in his business letter.

Find It

Look for the direct and indirect objects in the letter above. Underline the direct objects. Circle the indirect objects.

Write a letter to a friend to ask for some advice about school. Your paragraph should have four or five sentences. Include direct and indirect objects in your letter. Label direct objects DO; label indirect objects IO.

_____

_____

_____

_____

_____

_____

_____

_____

Fix It

The following sentences have misused pronouns as indirect objects. Rewrite the sentences with the correct pronouns as indirect objects.

1. Bob taught Sara and I to play the guitar.

_____

2. They gave she and I a surprise party.

_____

3. My parents built he and I a tree house in the backyard.

_____

4. Mr. Thomas called the boys and I in for dinner.

_____

Extra Practice

Lesson 7

Lesson 8

Lesson 9

• •

It is time to practice what you have learned. You have learned about compound indirect objects and indirect objects.

1. Which sentence below has a compound indirect object? Circle it.

   My sister is thirteen.

   Her favorite movie is *Titanic*.

   My mom gave my sister and me tickets to the movie.

   We loved it!

2. Underline the direct objects and circle the indirect objects in the following sentences.

   Matt mailed several well-known magazines and newspapers a letter about his annual dinner party.

   One magazine for gourmet chefs sent our amateur cook an extremely complimentary reply.

   Mark is submitting *Northwest Palate* magazine and *The Boston Globe* a 500-word article.

3. Put a check by the sentences that have a compound indirect object.

4. Write three sentences with an indirect object that names for whom the action was done.

   _____

   _____

5. Write a letter to the editor of your local newspaper about a problem in your neighborhood. Use some compound direct and indirect objects.

_____

_____

_____

_____

_____

_____

_____

_____

_____

_____

_____

_____

_____

_____

_____

_____

_____

6. Underline the direct objects and circle the indirect objects in your letter.

7. How many compound indirect objects did you use? _____

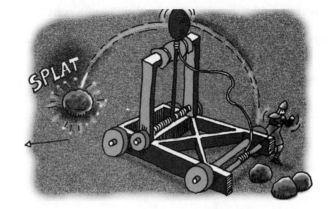

Lesson 10

Review

1. Fill in the blanks for each sentence.

A transitive verb is usually followed by a(n) _____.

Intransitive verbs do not have _____.

A _____ receives the action of the verb.

The _____ indirectly receives the action of the _____.

The _____ tells *to whom* or *for whom* the action has been carried out.

A compound direct object consists of _____ direct objects joined by a

_____.

A _____ indirect object consists of two or more _____ joined by a
conjunction.

2. Draw two lines under the transitive verbs. Circle the direct object.

In Egypt, Archimedes studied science and mathematics.

He defined the principle of the lever.

He designed the catapult.

He invented the hydraulic screw and compound pulley.

Rome invaded Syracuse during the Punic Wars.

Archimedes gave Syracuse his plans for the catapult.

He contributed much to science and math.

3. Write a paragraph about one of the topics below, or choose your own topic. Draw two lines under the transitive verbs. Underline any direct objects, and circle any indirect objects.

You may choose from these topics: *television, automobiles,* and *computers.*

_____

_____

_____

_____

_____

_____

4. Archimedes had another invention for use in war. Imagine that he wrote this part of a letter. Read through it first, then follow the directions.

Dear Gentlemen,

I would like to offer one of my inventions to you. I call it a mirror system. I have drawn a diagram for you. It is enclosed. Mirrors will reflect and intensify the sun's rays and destroy ships. Please send your answer to me.

Rewrite the paragraph, changing prepositional phrases to indirect objects when you can.

_____

_____

_____

_____

_____

5. Write a sentence with a compound direct object.

_____

_____

6. Write a sentence with a compound indirect object.

_____

_____

Lesson 1

Predicates with Linking Verbs

A linking verb connects the subject of a sentence to a noun, pronoun, or adjective.

Learn It

1. Read this.

Lynne   is   my sister.
| | |
subject   linking   word group that identifies
             verb   or describes the subject

A *linking verb* links the subject to a word or word group in the predicate that identifies or describes the subject.

The verbs *am, is, are, be, was, were, feel, look, prove, remain, resemble, sound, stay, become, grow, turn, smell,* and *taste* can be used as linking verbs.

2. Underline the linking verbs in the sentences below.

At the beach, Lynne feels happy.

The wind tastes slightly salty.

She became excited at the smell of the sea.

Find It

Underline the linking verbs in these sentences. Write the subject on the blank line. Draw two lines under the word or word group that the linking verb links to the subject.

Lynne's hometown is Orlando, Florida. _____

Orlando seems warm and comfortable. _____

In December, the weather feels cold. _____

Tampa seems friendlier. _____

After a while, Lynne grows tired. _____

Write three sentences with linking verbs.

_____

_____

_____

_____

_____

_____

Fix It

1. Finish the following sentences with predicate nouns or adjectives.

   The dinner smelled _____

   The water appeared _____

   The farmer's crops grew _____

   Mr. Jones is _____

   The dog is _____

   The girls are _____

2. These linking verbs don't fit in the sentences. Cross out any that appear wrong and write a better linking verb on the blank line.

   Angel are a toy poodle. _____

   She grows small. _____

   She remains fluffy. _____

   Her bark becomes noisy. _____

   She resembles so cute. _____

Name _____ Date _____ Class _____

Lesson 2

What Is a Predicate Noun?

A linking verb connects the subject to a complement.

1. Read these sentences.

   Orlando is <u>a city in Florida.</u>

   Disney World has been <u>a popular attraction for years.</u>

   Walt Disney was <u>the man who built Disney World.</u>

   A linking verb links the subject to a *complement*. A complement completes the predicate. A *predicate noun* is a complement that identifies the subject. It is sometimes called a *predicate nominative*.

2. Read the above sentences again and circle the linking verbs.

3. Each of the above sentences has a complement that identifies the subject. What are the two names for the complement?

   _____   _____

4. Write the predicate nouns in the above sentences.

   _____

   _____

   _____

5. Read these sentences. Circle any predicate nouns.

   She seems sad.

   He is the lucky winner of the contest.

   The girl in the blue pantsuit felt exhilarated.

   The twins were the subject of the short story.

Find It

Circle the linking verbs in these sentences. Underline the predicate nouns.

Tampa Bay is a large body of water.

The residents of Tampa are lucky people.

Fishing is a popular pastime for them.

Daytona Beach remains the home of the Daytona 500 NASCAR Race.

Dale Earnhardt was the winner of the race in 1998.

Try It

Write three sentences with linking verbs and predicate nouns.

_____

_____

_____

_____

_____

_____

Fix It

Here is a brochure about a tourist town. Fill in the blanks with predicate nouns.

Cozy Corners has become _____. It once was

_____. Lucinda Leach Peabody is _____

_____. She has invited people to tour the town. The most popular sight remains

_____. If you come, the best place to stay is _____

_____.

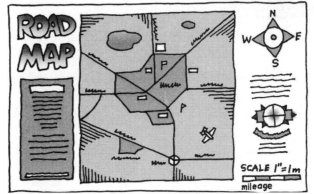

Unit 3

Lesson 3

Finding the Predicate Noun

A predicate noun identifies the subject.

Learn It

1. Read this sentence.

   A roadmap   is   an excellent tool for a traveler.

   subject   **linking verb**   **predicate noun**

   The *predicate noun* completes the predicate and identifies the subject.

   In the first sentence, *tool* is the predicate noun. It identifies the subject, *roadmap*. The predicate noun and the subject are connected by the linking verb *is*.

2. Underline the predicate noun in this sentence.

   The distance from Shady Grove to Pine Cone Lodge is three miles.

3. Circle the subject and draw two lines under the linking verb in the above sentence.

Find It

1. Underline the predicate noun in each of the following sentences.

   Inches and miles are both units of measurement.

   The mileage scale is the part of the map showing the ratio between inches and miles.

   The distance between the two points will be approximately twelve miles.

   These inches are really miles.

2. Circle the subjects in the above sentences.

3. Draw two lines under the linking verbs.

1. Write four sentences with predicate nouns and linking verbs.

_____

_____

_____

_____

_____

_____

_____

_____

2. Write the linking verbs that you used in your sentences on the blank lines below.

_____ _____ _____ _____

Fix It

1. Make each of these a sentence by adding a predicate noun. Choose predicate nouns from the box.

the housekeeper	Mrs. Williams	the front porch	the parlor	all conifers

The builder of Pine Cone Lodge was _____

The trees that surround the lodge are _____

The most popular room remains _____

Mr. Jones is _____

Surely, your favorite place to relax will be _____

2. List the linking verbs from the above sentences.

_____ _____ _____ _____ _____

3. Circle the subjects in the above sentences.

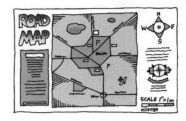

Extra Practice

Lesson 1 **Lesson 2** **Lesson 3**

It is time to practice what you have learned. You have learned about predicates with linking verbs, and predicate nouns (sometimes called *predicate nominatives*).

1. Write a sentence with a predicate noun with each of these linking verbs.

(am)

_____

_____

(resembles)

_____

_____

(were)

_____

_____

(was)

_____

_____

(is)

_____

_____

(are)

_____

_____

(will be)

_____

_____

2. Underline the predicate nouns in the sentences that you wrote.

3. Write a sentence with a predicate noun.

_____

_____

4. Circle the linking verb that you used in number 3.

5. Try your hand at poetry using linking verbs and predicate nouns.

_____

_____

_____

_____

_____

_____

_____

_____

_____

_____

_____

_____

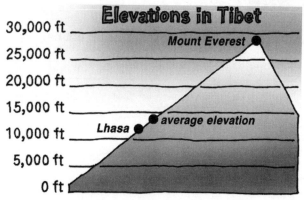

Lesson 4

Compound Predicate Nouns

You can combine sentences using compound predicate nouns.

Learn It

1. Read these sentences.

> **Tibet** *has been* an independent country.   **Tibet** *has been* a province of China.

> **Tibet** *has been* an independent country and a province of China.

You can make a *compound predicate noun* by combining two sentences with the same subject and verb.

2. Write the predicate nouns in the first two sentences.

_____   _____

3. Write the compound predicate noun in the last sentence.

_____

Find It

1. Underline the compound predicate nouns and draw two lines under the linking verbs in these sentences.

> The two large countries bordering Tibet are China and India.

> Tibet's most striking features are tall mountains and deep valleys.

> The most popular tourist attractions remain the capital city of Lahsa and Mount Everest.

> Many young men in Tibet become lamas or monks.

> The two leaders of Tibet were the Dalai Lama and the Panchen Lama.

2. Circle the subjects in the above sentences.

Write three sentences with compound predicate nouns.

_____

_____

_____

_____

_____

_____

Fix It

Combine these sentences to make one sentence with a compound predicate noun.

Tibet is a land-locked country. Tibet is the home of the Dalai Lama.

_____

_____

The Dalai Lama remains the religious leader for the Tibetans. The Dalai Lama remains a popular speaker.

_____

_____

The country is mostly sparse grassland between high mountain ranges. The country is mostly a high plateau of 16,000 ft.

_____

_____

A common food is barley. A common food is yak butter.

_____

Tibet remains a Shangri-La. Tibet remains a country full of secrets.

_____

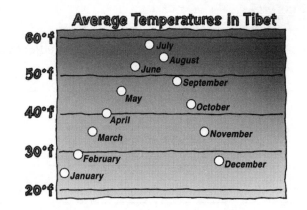

What Is a Predicate Adjective?

A predicate adjective describes the subject.

1. Read these sentences.

Tibet is remote.

The climate is cold.

Their hot tea with yak butter tastes strange.

A *predicate adjective* completes the predicate and describes the subject. A linking verb connects the predicate adjective to the subject. A complement can include adverbs, predicate adjectives, and prepositional phrases.

2. Underline the predicate adjectives and draw two lines under the linking verbs in the above sentences.

3. Circle the subjects in the above sentences.

Find It

1. Underline the predicate adjectives and draw two lines under the linking verbs in the following sentences.

The country of Tibet is mountainous.

Weather in this remote land appears extreme.

The temperature grows colder at night.

The temperature range will be great during any 24-hour period.

The temperatures in river valleys seem moderate compared to those in the mountains.

2. Circle the subjects in the above sentences.

Try It

Write four sentences with linking verbs and predicate adjectives.

_____

_____

_____

_____

_____

_____

_____

_____

Fix It

1. Fill in the blanks. Choose complements from the box below.

ready to go home	exhausted	warm during the day
cold	hard	cool

My favorite place to vacation is the mountains. The nights often become

_____. The temperatures grow _____.

We love to hike in the mountains. Some of the hiking trails seem _____.

Hikers often become _____. At the end of our vacation, we always feel

_____.

2. List the linking verbs in the above sentences.

_____   _____   _____   _____   _____

_____

Unit 3

Lesson 6

Compound Predicate Adjectives

You can combine sentences using
compound predicate adjectives.

Learn It

1. Read these sentences.

   Today the weather *seems* colder.   **Today the weather** *seems* windier.

   Today the weather *seems* colder and windier.

   **You can make a *compound predicate adjective* by combining two sentences with the same
   subject and verb.**

2. Write the predicate adjectives in the first two sentences.

   _____   _____

3. Write the compound predicate adjective in the last sentence. _____

Find It

1. Underline the compound predicate adjectives and draw two lines under the linking verb in each
   sentence.

   In July, the days become warm and sunny.

   This statement is true or false.

   The month of July in Australia is often cold or rainy.

   To Alaskans, a barbecue at the beach on Christmas day seems strange and unusual.

   For Australians, such a trip is natural and common.

2. Circle the subject in each of the sentences above.

Try It

Write four sentences with linking verbs and compound predicate adjectives.

_____

_____

_____

_____

_____

_____

_____

_____

Fix It

1. Finish these sentences with compound predicate adjectives.

Nights in the mountains are _____

As you near the equator, the days grow _____

Tomorrow the skies will be _____

During a tornado, the wind sounds _____

During a hurricane, the rain appears _____

On a cold winter night, the fireplace seems _____

2. Write the linking verbs for each sentence on the blank lines below.

_____   _____   _____

_____   _____   _____

Extra Practice

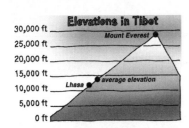

Lesson 4

Average Temperatures in Tibet

Lesson 5

Lesson 6

Practice It

It is time to practice what you have learned. You have learned about compound predicate nouns, predicate adjectives, and compound predicate adjectives.

1. Write three sentences, each with a compound predicate noun.

_____

_____

_____

_____

_____

_____

2. Write two sentences, each with a predicate adjective.

_____

_____

_____

_____

3. Combine these sentences to make compound predicate adjectives.

The soup tasted sweet. The soup tasted sour.

_____

_____

The basketball players appear tall. The basketball players appear graceful.

_____

The singing bells sounded sad. The singing bells sounded sorrowful.

_____

The truck proved too tall for the bridge. The truck proved too heavy for the bridge.

_____

4. Write a short composition on one of the following topics. Include compound predicate adjectives.

camping trip	a hiking trip
your favorite sport	an animal that interests you
a hobby that you enjoy	

_____

_____

_____

_____

_____

_____

_____

_____

_____

_____

_____

_____

_____

Predicate Nouns and Adjectives

Predicate nouns identify the subject.
Predicate adjectives describe the subject.

Learn It

1. Read these sentences.

   The caterpillar becomes a butterfly.

   The butterfly appears beautiful.

   Artificial butterflies are popular decorations.

   Butterflies are beautiful as they flutter among the flowers.

   Both predicate nouns and predicate adjectives complete the predicate. A predicate noun identifies the subject. A predicate adjective describes the subject.

2. Underline the predicate nouns and circle the predicate adjectives in the above sentences.

3. Draw two lines under the linking verbs and three lines under the subject.

Find It

1. In the following sentences, underline the predicate nouns and circle the predicate adjectives. Draw two lines under the linking verbs.

   The weather grows colder in the morning.

   The water becomes ice.

   The skating pond is a very popular place.

   The children feel happy to be there.

2. Draw three lines under the subject in each sentence.

1. Write two sentences with linking verbs and predicate nouns.

   _____

   _____

   _____

2. Write two sentences with linking verbs and predicate adjectives.

   _____

   _____

   _____

3. Write the linking verbs from your sentences on the blank lines.

   _____   _____   _____   _____

Fix It

1. Add linking verbs to these sentences.

   My sister _____ a dedicated athlete. She _____ an ice skater.

   Last year, she _____ fortunate to win the Junior State Championship.

   Next year she _____ too old to enter this contest.

2. Write any predicate nouns from the sentences above on the blank lines below.

   _____   _____

3. Write any predicate adjectives that you find on the blank lines below.

   _____

   _____

Lesson 8

Using Predicate Nouns and Adjectives

Predicate nouns and predicate adjectives can improve your writing.

Learn It

1. Read this paragraph.

> The stars appear bright overhead as the little coyote howls. It is a female coyote.
>
> I wonder if she has pups. She appears a shadow in the still darkness of the high desert night.
>
> The patter of her small paws seems closer now. My little dog looks alert. He cocks his head
>
> to one side. We remain calm. She seems hesitant on the edge of the circle of light from the
>
> campfire. My little dog sniffs and stretches. She turns. She becomes engulfed by the darkness.

Linking verbs and complements —both predicate nouns and predicate adjectives— are some of the tools used by writers.

2. In the paragraph above, draw two lines under the linking verbs. Underline the predicate adjectives and circle the predicate nouns.

Find It

In this paragraph, circle the linking verbs and underline the predicate adjectives.

> Stars appear twinkling in the cold, night sky. I look at them from my sleeping bag.
>
> The air feels crisp against my cheeks. Its coldness stings my eyes. The tears taste salty. I
>
> wipe them away with the edge of the bag. Now one star seems brighter. Maybe it is the
>
> North Star.

Write a short paragragh describing some event in your life. Underline any predicate nouns and adjectives.

_____

_____

_____

_____

_____

_____

_____

_____

Fix It

Rewrite your paragraph by adding more predicate nouns and adjectives.

_____

_____

_____

_____

_____

Lesson 9

More about Predicate Nouns and Predicate Adjectives

Learn It

1. Read this.

> High nimbus clouds appear fluffy and white. I run giggling through the soft grass in my bare feet. The soft rain feels fresh and cool. The tiny drops dampen my curly hair. This is Puerto Rico and my home. Puerto Rico is a land of sunshine and soft rain and a country with many colors. The raindrops look sparkling and crystal clear in the clean, green grass. This light rain comes every afternoon at the same time. The sun shines, but it also rains at the same time. It remains a mystery and a miracle to me to this day.

   Linking verbs, predicate nouns, and predicate adjectives are some of the tools used by writers.

2. Draw two lines under the linking verbs. Underline the predicate adjectives and circle the predicate nouns. Some may be compound predicate adjectives and compound predicate nouns. Put a **C** above the compound predicate adjectives or compound predicate nouns.

Find It

Circle the linking verbs. Underline the compound predicate nouns and adjectives.

   The corn grows tall and green.

   The green chile stew tastes hot and spicy.

   The dancers are Roberta and Alex.

Write a short composition describing some event in your life. Underline any predicate nouns and adjectives.

_____

_____

_____

_____

_____

_____

_____

_____

Fix It

Rewrite your composition and add compound predicate nouns and adjectives.

_____

_____

_____

_____

_____

_____

_____

_____

_____

Extra Practice

Lesson 7

Lesson 8

Lesson 9

Practice It

It is time to practice what you have learned. You have learned that predicate nouns identify a subject and that predicate adjectives describe a subject. You have also learned that linking verbs, predicate nouns, and predicate adjectives are some of the tools used by writers.

1. Write three sentences with predicate adjectives.

_____

_____

_____

_____

_____

_____

2. Write three sentences with predicate nouns.

_____

_____

_____

_____

_____

_____

3. Write a short composition with predicate adjectives, predicate nouns, compound predicate adjectives, and compound predicate nouns. Put **PA** above predicate adjectives, **PN** above predicate nouns, and **C** above the compound predicate nouns and adjectives.

_____

_____

_____

_____

_____

_____

_____

_____

_____

_____

_____

_____

_____

_____

_____

_____

_____

_____

Name _____ Date _____ Class _____

Lesson 10

Review

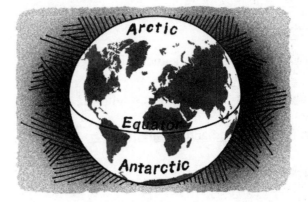

Review It

1. Fill in the blanks with linking verbs.

Evenings in the mountains _____ cool. To the weary campers, the bonfire

_____ comforting. The dish of pork and beans _____ a filling meal.

The piercing yowl of a mountain lion _____ frightening. Thankfully, the

mountain lion _____ afraid of the bonfire.

2. The main linking verbs in English are the **be** verbs. Write the **be** verbs on the blank lines below.

_____   _____   _____

_____   _____   _____

3. Write six other linking verbs on the blank lines below.

_____ _____ _____ _____ _____ _____

4. These verbs link the _____ of the sentence to _____

and _____.

5. A predicate noun identifies _____. A predicate adjective _____
the subject.

6. A compound predicate noun is _____ joined by a
conjunction.

7. A compound predicate _____ is two or more predicate adjectives joined by a

_____.

8. Name the part of the sentence that is underlined. Write your answer on the blank line.

In many areas of the world, the weather <u>is</u> _____ extremely cold. Two of

those areas are <u>the Arctic and Antarctic.</u> _____

The weather never grows <u>warm</u> _____ enough to melt the snow and ice.

Along the equator, temperatures <u>remain</u> _____ fairly constant. The days are

almost always <u>hot and sunny.</u> _____ The explanation for

this <u>is</u> _____ the <u>tilt</u> _____ of the earth's axis.

9. Write a composition about summer and winter. Include linking verbs, predicate nouns, and
predicate adjectives. Include at least one compound predicate noun or one compound predicate
adjective.

_____

_____

_____

_____

_____

_____

_____

_____

_____

_____

_____

_____

Name _____ Date _____ Class _____

Lesson 1

Identifying Phrases

A phrase is a group of words without a subject, a predicate, or both.

Learn It

1. Read these sentences.

   In the United States, people use *Fahrenheit thermometers.*

   Water freezes *at 32 degrees Fahrenheit.*

   Water should be boiling *at 212 degrees Fahrenheit.*

   A phrase is a group of words that form a unit. There are noun phrases, verb phrases, and prepositional phrases. They can be used as subjects, verbs, objects, adjectives, or adverbs in a sentence. A sentence may have more than one phrase. A phrase is not a sentence because a phrase does not have both a subject and a predicate.

2. Circle the phrases in the sentences in number 1.

3. Now read this.

   "Where did you go?"   "The beach."

   "What did you do?"   "Went swimming."

   Phrases are often used when answering questions.

   The beach is a noun phrase. It is not a complete sentence because _____.

   Went swimming is a verb phrase. It is not a complete sentence because it has no _____.

   When we write a short answer like this, we begin it with a capital letter and end it with a

   _____, just like a sentence.

Find It

1. Find two phrases in one of your textbooks and write them on the blank lines below.

   _____

   _____

2. Look at each of the phrases that you wrote and make sure they do not have both a subject and a predicate.

Try It

1. Underline any phrases in the following sentences.

   In the United Kingdom, people use Celsius thermometers.

   Water freezes at zero degrees Celsius.

   Water boils at 100 degrees Celsius.

   A daytime temperature of 30°C is 86 degrees on the Fahrenheit thermometer.

   Thirty degrees is a very hot temperature for people in London.

   Celsius thermometers are used in most Eastern Hemisphere countries.

2. Write two sentences with phrases.

   _____

   _____

   _____

   _____

3. Write two phrases.

   _____

   _____

Fix It

Add noun phrases, verb phrases, and prepositional phrase to the following.

_____, the United States has said it would convert from the English system

of measurements _____. Americans _____

making this conversion. _____ are just too used to our system of

feet, inches, cups, and quarts!

Lesson 2

Prepositions

Prepositions join nouns or pronouns to other words in a sentence.

Read these sentences.

Estimates of temperature can be used at the beach but not in the kitchen.

Temperatures soared today into the 100s.

Bake the cake batter at 350 degrees.

A *preposition* links *nouns* and *pronouns* to other words in a sentence. The word *preposition* comes from Latin words that mean to place before. In English, a preposition usually comes before a noun or a pronoun.

Some Common Prepositions

about	around	beside	down	into	since	until
above	as	between	during	of	through	up
across	at	beyond	for	on	to	upon
after	before	but	from	out	toward	with
among	below	by	in	outside	under	within

You may notice that *but, as, for,* and many other words on this list can be both prepositions and conjunctions. In fact, all conjunctions started in Old English as prepositions.

Find It

1. List the prepositions from the illustration for this lesson.

   _____ _____ _____

2. List the prepositions in the sentences from "Learn It."

   _____ _____ _____

   _____ _____

1. Underline the prepositions in the following sentences.

Beverly Sharp was baking a cake on her husband's birthday.

Her recipe from England read, "Set the oven at 175 degrees Celsius."

She couldn't find a conversion chart for Celsius and Fahrenheit temperatures.

After a while she gave up and estimated the temperature in degrees Fahrenheit.

Unfortunately, Beverly's cake burned in the oven.

2. Write five sentences with prepositions in them.

_____

_____

_____

_____

_____

_____

_____

_____

Fix It

Complete the following sentences by putting prepositions in the blanks.

Here's how you convert degrees Celsius _____ degrees Fahrenheit.

Multiply the number _____ degrees Celsius by 1.8 and then add 32.

You can buy conversion charts _____ some stores.

That will make things easier _____ you.

_____ a quick estimate, you can round 1.8 off to 2.

However, this will not work well _____ the kitchen.

Lesson 3

Prepositional Phrases

Prepositional phrases modify other words in a sentence.

Read these sentences.

> Abe Lincoln traveled *by raft down the Mississippi River.*

> The Mississippi River was a main source *of travel for thousands of years.*

A prepositional phrase is a group of words that starts with a preposition and is followed by a noun or a pronoun. This noun or pronoun is called the *object of the preposition.* There may be other words such as adjectives and adverbs between the preposition and the object.

Prepositional phrases act like either adjectives or adverbs in sentences.

1. Underline the prepositional phrases in these sentences.

> The Mississippi River flows down the middle of the United States.

> It has been the site of many stories, songs, and movies.

> It starts in Lake Itasca, Minnesota, and empties into the Gulf of Mexico.

> Frontiersmen from the Northwest took goods on large wooden rafts to New Orleans, Louisiana, near the end of the river.

> The rafts could not go up the Mississippi against the current.

> In New Orleans, the frontiersmen broke the rafts apart and sold the wood as lumber.

2. Circle the object of the preposition in each prepositional phrase that you underlined.

1. Write three sentences with prepositional phrases.

_____

_____

_____

_____

2. Write the objects of the prepositions from your sentences on the blank lines below.

_____   _____   _____

3. Write a sentence with a prepositional phrase that acts like an adverb.

_____

_____

4. Write a sentence with a prepositional phrase that acts like an adjective.

_____

_____

5. Circle the objects of the preposition in each of the sentences above that you wrote.

1. Complete these sentences with prepositional phrases.

The Mississippi River starts _____.

The city of New Orleans is located _____.

Huckleberry Finn is a book _____.

Rafts floated _____.

2. Circle the object of the preposition in each of the sentences above.

Extra Practice

Lesson 1

Lesson 2

Lesson 3

Practice It

It is time to practice what you have learned. You have learned about phrases, prepositions, and prepositional phrases, and their use as sentence modifiers.

1. Underline the prepositional phrases in these sentences.

> Two kinds of thermometers are used in the world today.
>
> A thermometer in most countries tells the temperature in degrees Celsius.
>
> In the United States, thermometers tell the temperature in degrees Fahrenheit.
>
> Measurement of temperature is of great importance in science and in medicine.

2. Write a sentence that includes a phrase.

_____

_____

3. Write two noun phrases.

_____   _____

4. Write ten prepositions on the blank lines below.

_____   _____   _____   _____

_____   _____   _____   _____

5. Write a sentence that includes a prepositional phrase.

_____

_____

6. Write two sentences that include prepositional phrases that act as adjectives.

_____

_____

_____

_____

7. Underline the prepositional phrases in these sentences.

Abe Lincoln was born in a log cabin in Kentucky on February 12, 1809.

His family moved to a farm in Indiana when Abe was 8.

They moved to Illinois in 1830.

He went to school for less than a year.

When Abe was 19, he was hired to go down the Mississippi River to New Orleans

on a flatboat, a kind of raft used on rivers.

When the family moved to Illinois, he worked splitting logs into fence rails.

Later, when he was running for political office, he was sometimes called "the rail splitter."

Abe became a lawyer in another lawyer's office.

In 1861, at the age of 52, he became the 16th president of the United States.

8. Circle the object of the preposition in each of the prepositional phrases that you found.

9. Write a paragraph about someone you admire. Include prepositional phrases.

_____

_____

_____

_____

_____

10. Underline the prepositional phrases in your paragraph.

11. How many of your prepositional phrases acted as adjectives? _____

12. Circle the object of the preposition for each phrase.

13. How many of your prepositional phrases acted as adverbs? _____

Name _____ Date _____ Class _____

Lesson 4

Finding Prepositional Phrases

A prepositional phrase can act like an adjective or adverb and appear anywhere in a sentence.

1. Read these sentences.

   In 1803, the United States agreed to pay France 15 million dollars *for the Louisiana Territory.*

   France needed money to continue its war in Europe.

   A prepositional phrase is a group of words that starts with a preposition and includes a noun or pronoun.

   A prepositional phrase may come anywhere in a sentence. It acts as a modifier.

   The phrase *In 1803* modifies *agreed* and tells when.

   The phrase *for the Louisiana Territory* modifies *dollars* and tells what the money was for.

   The phrase *to pay* looks like a prepositional phrase but is not. *Pay* is a verb, not a noun or pronoun.

2. Underline the prepositional phrase in the second example sentence from number 1.

Underline the prepositional phrases in these sentences.

By 1800, many settlers had reached the Mississippi River.

Thomas Jefferson was chosen to become our third president in 1801.

By 1803, four more states had been added to our country.

In 1804, President Jefferson sent Lewis and Clark to explore the West.

Their party started from St. Louis and traveled up the Missouri River and into the wilderness.

They were guided by Sacajawea, a Shoshone woman who also served as an interpreter.

Lewis and Clark crossed the Rocky Mountains and then went down the Columbia River.

They got to the Pacific Ocean in November, 1805.

1. Look at each prepositional phrase that you underlined in "Find It."

   Which ones tell us when?

   _____   _____   _____

   _____   _____

   Which ones tell us where?

   _____   _____   _____

   _____   _____

2. Write three sentences. Include at least two prepositional phrases in each.

   _____

   _____

   _____

   _____

   _____

   _____

   _____

Use the prepositions from the box to fill in the blanks below.

beside	on	under	until	during

Lewis and Clark traveled _____ the Missouri River.

In October of 1804 they built Fort Mandan _____ the banks of the river.

The party stayed there _____ the winter.

Sacajawea became their scout and stayed with them _____ the end.

The expedition crossed the Continental Divide _____ harsh conditions.

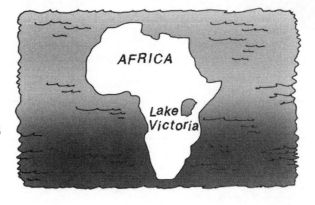

Lesson 5

Sentences with Prepositional Phrases

Prepositional phrases are important
writing tools.

Read these sentences.

> The continent of Africa lies off the southern coast of Europe.

> It is the home of some of the oldest civilizations on Earth.

Prepositional phrases are one of the most common ways to add additional information in a sentence. They can tell possession, location, source, time, manner, cause, and purpose.

The continent lies hardly says anything. Look at how much information the phrases *of Africa* and *off the southern coast of Europe* add to the sentence.

Use prepositional phrases to add more meaning to your sentences.

Underline the prepositional phrases in these sentences.

> Africa is the second largest continent in the world.

> Africa also has the second largest population in the world.

> In Africa is found the oldest evidence of human life.

> Some of the world's earliest and richest civilizations developed there.

> Lake Victoria is the largest lake in Africa.

> Lake Victoria is the second largest freshwater lake in the world.

> Millions of Africans depend on the fish from this lake.

> There are more than 400 species of fish in Lake Victoria.

> The largest group consists mostly of a fish called a cichlid.

> The addition of Nile perch was helpful because it ate the cichlids.

> Nile perch come from the Nile River in Egypt.

Write a short report about an animal. Underline any prepositional phrases.

_____

_____

_____

_____

_____

Fix It

Below are some simple sentences. Rewrite them, adding at least one prepositional phrase to each.

Lakes provide fish.

_____

_____

Fishermen sell fish.

_____

_____

They ship the fish.

_____

_____

People pay the fishermen.

_____

_____

Big fish are more valuable.

_____

_____

Lesson 6

Subjects with Prepositional Phrases

Prepositional phrases can modify the subjects in sentences.

1. Read these sentences.

   Farmers grow 90 percent of the world's rice.

   Farmers *in India, China, and Japan* grow 90 percent of the world's rice.

   The subject in the first sentence lacks important information. The prepositional phrase in the subject in the second sentence makes it much more informative.

2. Look in a book and find three examples of sentences with subjects modified by prepositional phrases. Write these prepositional phrases on the blank lines below.

   _____

   _____

   _____

3. Circle the object of the preposition in each of the prepositional phrases that you wrote.

1. Underline the prepositional phrase that modifies the subjects of each of these sentences.

   The people of India use rice as a main source of food.

   The crops in this country are affected by the amount of rainfall they receive.

   Monsoon rains at the wrong time can ruin the crops.

   Monsoon rains in the Eastern Hemisphere are like hurricanes in the Western Hemisphere.

   The power of nature plays an important role in the production of crops.

2. Circle the objects of the prepositions that you underlined.

Try It

Write three sentences with prepositional phrases modifying the subject.

_____

_____

_____

_____

_____

_____

Fix It

1. These subjects do not have prepositional phrases. Add prepositional phrases to give additional information to these subjects.

    The coast _____

    Many trees _____

    The boats _____

2. Write complete sentences with the subjects and phrases above.

    _____

    _____

    _____

    _____

    _____

    _____

3. Write the objects of the prepositions from number one on the blank lines below.

    _____   _____   _____

Extra Practice

Lesson 4   **Lesson 5**   **Lesson 6**

It is time to practice what you have learned. You have learned that a prepositional phrase may come anywhere in a sentence, adds information to the subject, and can make sentences more informative.

1. Underline the prepositional phrases in these sentences.

   At the time, going across the continent seemed logical.

   In St. Louis, Lewis and Clark prepared for the long journey.

   In May, the party was ready to leave.

   They floated down rivers and climbed up mountains on their way to the Pacific.

   In November of the following year they finally reached the Pacific.

   Sacajawea guided them and helped them to talk to the Indians they met on the way.

2. Write a sentence that uses a prepositional phrase that shows *where*.

   _____

   _____

3. Write a sentence that uses a prepositional phrase that shows *when*.

   _____

   _____

4. Write a sentence that uses a prepositional phrase that shows *from where* or *what*.

   _____

   _____

5. Write a sentence that uses a prepositional phrase that shows possession.

_____

_____

6. Write a sentence that uses a prepositional phrase that shows *how*.

_____

_____

7. Write a sentence that uses a prepositional phrase that shows *cause* or *purpose*.

_____

_____

8. Write a sentence with a prepositional phrase modifying the subject.

_____

_____

9. Write the object of the preposition for each of the prepositional phrases that you wrote in numbers 2–8.

_____   _____   _____

_____   _____   _____

_____

10. Write a prepositional phrase with the word *to*.

_____

_____

Unit 4

Lesson 7

Predicates with Prepositional Phrases

Prepositional phrases can modify the verbs in sentences.

Learn It

1. Read these sentences.

    Napoleon *needed money for his campaigns in Europe, Asia, and Africa.*

    He offered to sell the Louisiana Territory to the United States.

    Prepositional phrases in the predicate also give additional information. The predicate usually begins with a verb and includes everything after it.

2. Find the predicate in the second sentence. Underline any prepositional phrases that you find.

3. Circle the objects of the prepositions in each sentence.

Find It

1. Underline the prepositional phrases in the predicates of these sentences.

    Napoleon took his troops to Egypt in 1798.

    Turkey ruled Egypt at this time.

    Napoleon defeated the Turks with ease.

    France was also at war with Britain during this period.

    Admiral Nelson defeated the fleet of France.

    Napoleon's army became stranded in Egypt.

    Napoleon left Egypt secretly in October of 1799.

    In November he took command of the French government as its only leader.

    Napoleon had himself crowned the emperor of France.

2. Circle the object of the preposition in each of the prepositional phrases that you underlined.

Try It

Write five sentences with prepositional phrases in the predicate.

_____

_____

_____

_____

_____

_____

_____

_____

_____

_____

Fix It

1. Finish these sentences by adding prepositional phrases. Use the information from "Find It."

   Napoleon led an expedition _____.

   He defeated the Turks _____.

   The French fleet was defeated _____.

   Napoleon became _____.

   He was crowned Emperor _____.

2. Write the object of the preposition for each of the prepositional phrases that you wrote in number one.

   _____   _____   _____   _____   _____

Lesson 8

Writing Book and Movie Titles

The titles of most published words are written in special ways.

Learn It

Read these sentences.

Karl read the book *What's the Deal?: Jefferson, Napoleon, and the Louisiana Purchase.*

Last night I watched a movie on cable called *Napoleon the Conqueror.*

Titles of books, movies, and major works are placed in italics. If you do not have a computer, you should underline them.

Major works may include a scholarly journal, magazine, newspaper, government report, play, musical, opera, or other long musical composition, television show, radio program, or long poem.

Capitalize the first and last word of a title and all the words in between except for *a, an, the,* prepositions, and conjunctions.

Find It

Underline the book and movie titles in the sentences below. Add capitals where needed.

Ms. Blumberg also wrote Commodore Perry in the land of the shogun.

Karl's father read a book entitled Napoleon bonaparte by Alan Schom.

A new book, assassination at St. helena revisited, tells about Napoleon's last days.

Two movies about Napoleon are Desiree and battle of Waterloo.

A recent jeopardy TV program had a whole category on Napoleon.

I used the World book encyclopedia to find out more about Napoleon's career.

1. Finish these sentences with book or movie titles. Underline the titles and pay attention to capitalization.

   My favorite book is _____.

   My favorite movie is _____.

   The title of my math book is _____.

   The last book I read was _____.

   The last movie I saw was _____.

2. Write two sentences with titles of movies, books, or other major works.

   _____

   _____

   _____

Rewrite the sentences below using the rules in this lesson for capitalization and underlining.

Karl decided to read Rhoda Blumberg's book, the incredible journey of lewis and clark.

_____

_____

He also wants to read the story, sacajawea, guide to lewis and clark.

_____

_____

Jenna would like to see the movie, the last of the mohicans.

_____

_____

Name _____ Date _____ Class _____

Lesson 9

Making Better Sentences

Computers make it easier for all of us to be authors.

Learn It

Read this paragraph.

> Writing for me is a great joy. It gives me a chance to create an effect on others, and a chance to communicate my ideas. I am always delighted when someone reads what I have written and understands it. In the beginning, it can be tough getting started. What I usually do is to make notes as the ideas come to me. I store them on my computer. Every story is a little different. How do you write?

Really good writing means using everything you have learned so far. This includes using direct objects, indirect objects, predicate nouns, predicate adjectives, and prepositional phrases.

Find It

Read each of the sentences that were taken from the above paragraph. Write on the blank line whether the underlined word or phrase is a direct object, an indirect object, a predicate noun, a predicate adjective, or a prepositional phrase. The first one has been done for you.

Writing for me is a great <u>joy</u>. _____predicate noun_____

I am always <u>delighted</u> when someone reads what I have written and

understands it. _____

It gives <u>me</u> a chance to create an effect on others. _____

I store <u>them</u> on my computer. _____

<u>In the beginning</u>, it can be tough getting started. _____

Write a short paragraph of at least four sentences about something you enjoy.

_____

_____

_____

_____

_____

_____

_____

Fix It

Rewrite your paragraph to include all of the following at least once: direct object, indirect object, predicate noun, predicate adjective, and prepositional phrase.

_____

_____

_____

_____

_____

_____

_____

_____

_____

Extra Practice

Lesson 7

Lesson 8

Lesson 9

Practice It

It is time to practice what you have learned. You have learned that prepositional phrases are often used in the predicates of sentences to give additional information. You have also learned how to write titles of books, movies, plays, operas, and other long musical compositions, television shows, and radio programs. You have learned that good writers make use of direct and indirect objects, predicate nouns and predicate adjectives, and prepositional phrases.

1. Place a checkmark in front of the sentences below that have prepositional phrases in their predicates.

   The large number of enthusiastic students surprised the school principal.

   The students were especially enthusiastic about the new computers in the school library.

   The computers could help students find answers to many questions about the world and its nations.

   Many students in math class were eager to use the computers.

   History students could use them to learn more about events and people of the past.

   English classes could get more information about the authors whose books they were reading.

2. Write two sentences with a prepositional phrase in the predicate.

   _____

   _____

   _____

   _____

3. Write the object of the preposition for each of the sentences that you wrote.

   _____   _____

4. Write the names of two books you have read lately.

_____

_____

5. Write the name of your favorite television show or radio program. Use it in a sentence.

_____

_____

6. Circle the indirect object and underline the direct object in each of these sentences.

Napoleon gave the French people an encouraging victory in Egypt.

Later, Admiral Nelson's British fleet gave them a stinging defeat.

7. Circle the predicate nouns in these sentences.

Nelson was an English naval hero who won many victories at sea.

In 1796, Napoleon became commander of the French army in Italy.

8. Circle the predicate adjectives in these sentences.

Napoleon was Corsican, but Corsica had become part of France the year before he was born.

He was thin when he joined the army, but he became quite heavy as he grew older.

9. Write a paragraph about an activity, hobby, sport, or movie that you enjoy. Describe the activity and tell when and where you do it, and why you enjoy it.

_____

_____

_____

_____

_____

_____

10. Count the number of prepositional phrases that you used in your paragraph. How many did you write?

_____

Lesson 10

Review

These documents are important to
the liberty that we enjoy.

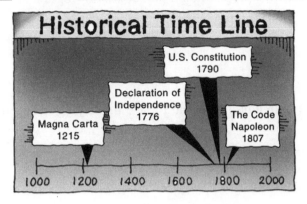

Review It

1. Fill in the blanks in this paragraph.

A _____ is a group of words that does not include a

_____ or a _____. A preposition is a word that introduces

a _____. A prepositional phrase gives more information about the

_____ or _____. It is introduced by a _____

and contains a _____ or _____ but not a

_____. Prepositional phrases often tell _____ or

_____. The object of the preposition is the _____ or

_____ following the preposition. Titles of books and movies are

_____. All the words in the title are capitalized except _____,

_____, and _____. These are _____

if they are the _____ or _____ word in the title.

2. Underline the prepositional phrases in these sentences.

King John of England signed the Magna Carta in 1215.

The Magna Carta established the rights and duties of the king and his subjects.

It stated that not even the king is above the law.

The Magna Carta also set forth the principle of justice for all.

3. Write a sentence with a prepositional phrase modifying the subject.

_____

_____

4. Write a sentence with a prepositional phrase modifying the predicate.

_____

_____

5. Circle the object of the preposition in each of the sentences that you wrote.

6. Read the following paragraph. Add prepositions in the blanks. Capitalize and underline the titles of books or movies.

The meeting _____ our book club took place _____ July 30. We have been

discussing the book to kill a mockingbird by Harper Lee. The main character is a young girl

growing up _____ the South. Next month we will all read a tree grows in brooklyn.

This book is set _____ a large city. Samantha wondered why we are reading these

books when they have been made _____ movies. She said we could rent them

_____ the video store. Several members said that books can be more enjoyable.

7. Write a paragraph that includes each of the following: a direct object, an indirect object, a prepositional phrase, a predicate noun, and a predicate adjective.

_____

_____

_____

_____

_____

_____

_____

_____

Lesson 1

Past, Present, and Future Tenses

Verbs have three tenses.

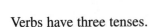

1. Read this sentence.

   Most marsupials *live* in Australia, New Zealand, and New Guinea.

   The tense of a verb shows the time of the action or state of being.

   Verbs can show three times: past, present, and future.

   The simple present tense is usually the base form of the verb. Use the simple present tense when talking or writing about something that happens regularly, states a fact or opinion, or describes creative works. You can also use it to indicate future action.

2. Read this sentence.

   The bandicoot *lived* in a pouch until it *was* older.

   Use the simple past tense to report an action that was completed in the past at a known time or to report past actions that no longer occur.

   The simple past tense of regular verbs is formed by adding *-ed* to the base form.

3. Read this sentence.

   A baby marsupial *will live* in its mother's pouch after birth.

   The simple future tense is made with the base form of the verb and *will*. Use the simple future tense to report a future event or state, to indicate willingness or intent to do something, and to indicate probability or expected action.

Write the tense of the verb after each sentence.

Blake and Kevin live in Auckland, New Zealand. _____

They will move to Sydney, Australia next year. _____

Last year they visited their aunt in Sydney. _____

One night, they observed a bandicoot in the brush. _____

Try It

Write one sentence each with the simple present, simple future, and simple past tenses of the verb *live*.

_____

_____

_____

_____

_____

Fix It

Rewrite this paragraph. Use the appropriate tenses of the verbs in parentheses.

Last year we (study) the countries of the South Pacific. I always (enjoy) learning about new places. After college, I (visit) as many of these places as I can. The Great Barrier Reef (stretch) for miles off the coast of Australia. If I'm lucky, I (snorkel) on the Great Barrier Reef.

_____

_____

_____

_____

_____

Lesson 2

How to Make Perfect Tenses

The perfect tenses include the present perfect, the past perfect, and the future perfect.

Learn It

1. Read these sentences.

The owl *has rested* all day.
present perfect tense

He *had hunted* for food the night before.
past perfect tense

By night, he *will have gathered* enough energy for another hunt.
future perfect tense

In addition to the simple tenses, English verbs have perfect tenses. The perfect tenses show a relationship between the time of events.

Study this chart on forming the perfect tenses.

Tense	How to Form It
present perfect	add *has* or *have* to the past participle: *has gone, have bought, has painted*
past perfect	add *had* to the past participle: *had gone, had bought, had painted*
future perfect	add *shall have* or *will have* to the past participle: *shall have gone, will have bought, shall have painted*

Find It

Underline the verbs that are in a perfect tense. Look for the forms of the helping verb *have*.

I didn't realize that I had left my porch light on all night. I have done this often. Moths love the light and collect around it. This summer many moths have served as food for small rodents that hunt at night. In turn, the owls eat the small rodents. By leaving the light on again tonight, I will have supplied food for many nocturnal creatures.

Other creatures that come out at night near my house are skunks, foxes and cats. I had seen lots of skunks in March, but fewer have come out since then. If my new neighbor's cat comes around tonight, I will have seen all the neighborhood cats.

Write one sentence with a verb in the present perfect tense, one sentence with a verb in the past perfect tense, and one sentence with a verb in the future perfect tense.

_____

_____

_____

_____

_____

_____

Fix It

Rewrite this paragraph using the present perfect, past perfect, or future perfect tense of the verbs in parentheses.

Bat Island, off the coast of Australia, (be) the home of fruit bats for many years. David (teach) at the University of Wisconsin. He (travel) to Bat Island in order to study these nocturnal creatures. During the day, he observed the bats nesting in the trees. Bats (learn) how to sleep hanging from branches. At night, David watched as clouds of bats filled the sky. They were heading to the mainland where they would feast on fruit.

_____

_____

_____

_____

_____

_____

_____

_____

Lesson 3

Present Perfect Tense

The present perfect tense expresses action which began in the past but continues or is completed in the present.

Learn It

Read these sentences.

Nocturnal creatures *have learned* to use senses other than sight.

Use the present perfect tense to report an action begun in the past and extending into the present.

I *have finished* writing my report on owls.

Use the present perfect tense to report a past action that relates to something in the present.

The owl *has eaten* a titmouse.

Use the present perfect tense to report an action completed at some unspecified time in the past.

The present perfect tense always uses *have* and *has* with the past participle of a verb.

Find It

1. Underline the verbs that are in the present perfect tense.

   Throughout time, creatures have adapted to their environment. The eyes of the owl have grown large to help it see at night. Some animals have gone through many changes. Adaptation occurs when the environment changes. Species who couldn't adapt have vanished. With very few exceptions, each individual animal is different from the rest. Most differences are not important. But some differences have given a few members of a group an advantage in adapting to a new environment. These animals have gotten more food or have escaped predators better than the others. The fittest animals have survived. The less fit have not.

2. What does the present perfect tense use?

_____

Write five sentences with verbs in the present perfect tense.

_____

_____

_____

_____

_____

_____

_____

_____

_____

Fix It

Change the base form of the verb in the parentheses to the present perfect tense.

David (choose) to study nocturnal animals.

_____

He and his friend (hide) in the bushes at night.

_____

Often, David (see) owls hunting at night.

_____

We (observe) small rodents foraging for seeds.

_____

David (write) all his observations in a notebook.

_____

Extra Practice

Lesson 1

Lesson 2

Lesson 3

Unit **5**

Practice It

It is time to practice what you have learned. You have learned about the simple present, simple past, and simple future tenses. You have also learned about the present perfect, past perfect, and future perfect tenses, and the special uses of the present perfect tense.

1. Identify the tenses in these sentences. Write the name of the tense on the blank line.

You have a new haircut! _____

Yes, the hairdresser cut it real short. _____

Is that the way you had wanted it to look? _____

Yes, it is. _____

By this time next week, I will have gotten a haircut myself. _____

My mom has gone twice to the new salon in the mall for her perm. _____

She liked the look of it both times. _____

I will tell my aunt about that salon. _____

She always looks for a new place for a dye job! _____

My father has dyed his hair for the last ten years. _____

He doesn't like his gray hair. _____

He will get a haircut and a dye job next week. _____

But he has always called the dye job a "tint." _____

2. Write four sentences in the present perfect tense.

_____

_____

_____

_____

_____

_____

3. Write a verb in a correct tense above each word in parentheses. There may be more than one correct answer.

Yesterday while I (walk) to the store I (see) a large pig in the middle of the street.

I always (enjoy) bird watching, especially when I (have) space to set up my spotting scope.

By the time Jose's father (get) back from San Diego, Jose (celebrate) his fourteenth birthday.

Nick's mother sometimes (drive) the Bentley limousines that her father (rent) for weddings.

4. Write a paragraph about something you like to do. Include some verbs in perfect tenses.

_____

_____

_____

_____

_____

_____

_____

Name _____ Date _____ Class _____

Lesson 4

Present Perfect Tense and Simple Present Tense

Learn It

Read these sentences.

> Coyotes *live* in a wash near my home.

> They *have lived* there as long as I can remember.

Use the simple present tense to express an action (or existence) which is happening now or which happens continually.

Use the present perfect tense to report an action was begun in the past but continues or is completed in the present.

Study these examples of sentences with simple present tense verbs and present perfect tense verbs.

Simple present tense	Present perfect tense
Coyotes *howl* outside every night. Coyotes *are becoming* rarer and rarer. Ranchers *hunt* coyotes that *attack* their livestock.	Coyotes *have howled* outside every night. Coyotes *have become* rarer and rarer. Ranchers *have hunted* coyotes that *have attacked* their livestock.

Find It

Underline the present tense verbs and circle the present perfect tense verbs below.

Coyotes usually stay in the wash behind my house. Some have come right up to our back patio. Our wall has kept them out so far. When our dog smells a coyote, he goes crazy. Coyotes have hunted domestic cats and small dogs. When a coyote encounters a human, it looks at the person and then casually walks away.

Write a paragraph about an animal. Use both the simple present and the present perfect tenses.

_____

_____

_____

_____

_____

_____

Fix It

Change the verb in parentheses to the simple present or the present perfect tense. Write the new paragraph below.

Sadly, some communities (drive) the coyotes away. Coyotes never (be) a major threat to humans. When a coyote (eat) his fill of small animals, he (go) back to his den and (sleep). I often (go) for a walk in the early morning. Sometimes I (meet) coyotes on their way home. They (stop) and (look) at me and then (saunter) away.

_____

_____

_____

_____

_____

_____

_____

Name _____   Date _____   Class _____

Lesson 5

Present Perfect Tense and Simple Past Tense

Read these sentences.

> Our friend Karla *read* a newspaper article about a raccoon many years ago.

> Karla *has* always *maintained* an interest in racoons.

Use the simple past tense to express an action (or existence) completed in the past. Use the present perfect tense to express an action that was begun in the past but continues or is completed in the present.

Study these examples of sentences with present perfect tense verbs and simple past tense verbs.

Present perfect tense (action begun in past but continues in present)	**Simple past tense** (action completed in past)
Karla *has seen* raccoons before.	Karla first *saw* raccoons three years ago.
She *has found* them climbing trees in her yard.	She *became* fascinated.
She *has been* fascinated by them for years.	She *bought* and *read* every book written about raccoons!

Here is the newspaper article that Karla read. Circle the past tense verbs and underline the present perfect verbs.

> The pond by Jesse Johnson's home has attracted raccoons for years. On his way home last night, Jesse saw a dead raccoon beside the road. A hollow tree near the pond has served as home for a number of raccoon families. Last week he spied a mother and three baby raccoons there. This morning Jesse went to the tree and found one baby raccoon. He took it home and their dog, Milly, adopted it. Jesse has looked for the other two baby raccoons, but he hasn't found them yet.

1. Write a short article using both the past tense and the present perfect tense.

_____

_____

_____

_____

_____

2. Write three sentences using the verb *break* in the present tense, the past tense, and the present perfect tense.

_____

_____

_____

_____

_____

_____

Fix It

1. Fill in the blanks using verbs in the past tense or the present perfect tense. Use these verbs: *grow, eat, identify,* and *find*.

   Scientists _____ seven species of raccoons. Raccoons

   belong to the same family as the pandas. Raccoons usually measure from 16 to 24 inches.

   Some _____ larger. Scientists once _____ a

   raccoon that was 36 inches long. That raccoon must _____ a lot of crayfish.

2. Reread the paragraph. List the verbs that are in the present tense.

   _____   _____

Lesson 6

Past Perfect Tense

A verb in the past perfect tense expresses action which began in the past and was completed in the past.

Learn It

Read these sentences.

> Due to a childhood illness, Helen Keller *became* deaf and blind at the age of two.

Use the simple tense to report an action definitely completed in the past.

> By the age of seven, Helen *had become* a big problem for her family.

Use the past perfect tense to say that an action was completed by a specified time in the past.

> By the time that Anne Sullivan arrived, Helen *had developed* some very unusual strategies for survival.

Use the past perfect tense to say that an action was completed by the time another action occurred.

> Her parents *had wanted* Helen to have a normal childhood.

Use the past perfect tense to report an unfulfilled hope or intention.

Use the verb *had* and a verb's past participle to form the past perfect tense.

Find It

Here is a paragraph about Helen Keller. Circle the past perfect verbs.

> The Keller family had tried to find a good tutor for their little girl Helen, but none of them stayed very long. Helen was blind and deaf. In addition, she had a terrible temper. Then Anne Sullivan came to work for the Keller family. She taught Helen to communicate with others. Before Anne did this, Helen had lived a life of solitude. By the time she died, Helen Keller had contributed much to the world. She had become a symbol of hope for people with disabilities.

1. Write a sentence with the verb *go* in the past perfect tense.

_____

_____

2. Write a sentence with the verb *be* in the past perfect tense.

_____

_____

3. Write a sentence with the verb *write* in the past perfect tense.

_____

_____

2. Write a sentence with the verb *speak* in the past perfect tense.

_____

_____

Fix It

Put each of the verbs in parentheses into the past perfect tense.

Helen Keller not (begin) to talk when she became deaf and blind.

_____

The Keller family (seek) help for many years.

_____

Helen never (speak) a word before Anne Sullivan taught her.

_____

By the time she died, Helen Keller (fly) all over the world and (give) many speeches.

_____

Extra Practice

Lesson 4

Lesson 5

Lesson 6

Practice It

It is time to practice what you have learned. You have learned the different uses of the present perfect and the past perfect tenses.

1. Read these sentences and circle the verbs in the present perfect tense.

   Darwin's 18th century research has interested me in the study of heredity.

   Marianne is interested only in ice skating and practices every day.

   Elly and George have bought a house which they are fixing up now.

   Mr. Mleczko has lived on Vernon Street as long as I can remember.

   His cats hissed and yowled at each other all night long.

2. Read these sentences and circle the verbs in the past perfect tense.

   When she had finished her research, Carmen sat down to write her report.

   I had never heard of Carl Sagan until I saw the movie, *Contact*.

   It was one of the most gripping films I have ever seen.

   Svetlana has always wanted to live on a houseboat.

   Skating in an ice show is something Marianne had wanted to do for a long time.

3. Write two short sentences using the present perfect tense.

   _____

   _____

   _____

   _____

4. Write two short sentences using the past perfect tense.

_____

_____

_____

_____

5. Write one or more paragraphs about what you might be when you grow up. Use a variety of verb tenses as they are needed.

_____

_____

_____

_____

_____

_____

_____

_____

6. Copy one sentence from your paragraph(s). Rewrite it, changing the tense of the verb to another tense.

_____

_____

_____

_____

7. Explain how this has changed the meaning of the sentence.

_____

_____

Lesson 7

Past Perfect Tense and Simple Past Tense

Learn It

1. Read these sentences.

> Explorers found a tomb in Egypt. Priests had carved hieroglyphics on the walls.

> Ancient Egyptians used hieroglyphics to record their history. Over time, people had lost the ability to read them.

The simple past tense expresses action or existence *completed at a specific time in the past*. **The past perfect tense** is used to express action *begun in the past and was completed in the past*.

Study these examples of sentences with simple past tense verbs and past perfect tense verbs.

Simple past tense (action completed in past)	Past perfect tense (action begun in past and finished in past)
Explorers *found* a tomb in Egypt.	Priests *had carved* hieroglyphics on the walls.
Ancient Egyptians *used* hieroglyphics to record their history.	Over time, people *had lost* the ability to read them.

Find It

Circle the past tense verbs and underline the past perfect tense verbs.

The French army remained in Egypt because Lord Nelson had destroyed their fleet.
Napoleon had never been a man to waste time. He ordered his soldiers to repair some
damaged buildings. One day a workman hit a stone with his shovel. Someone had carved
three messages on the stone. The messages were in Greek, demotic (a simplified form of
Egyptian writing), and hieroglyphics. Scholars saw the same Greek word in several places.
They studied the hieroglyphics and saw a repetition of symbols. They believed that someone
had carved the same message in three different languages. It took a number of years to make
this discovery. After many people had tried, Jean Champollion succeeded in 1921 in
translating hieroglyphics.

Write two sentences using both the past tense and the past perfect tense.

_____

_____

_____

_____

Fix It

Read this paragraph. Fill in the blanks with the correct form of the verb in parentheses.

In 1922, Howard Carter _____ (find) Tutankhamen's tomb.

The Egyptians _____ (bury) this pharaoh in 1325 B.C. They

_____ (hide) the tomb because vandals _____(destroy)

other tombs in the past. Archaeologists _____ (search) for the tomb

for many years without success until Carter _____ (discover) it.

Some workers _____ (refuse) to help Carter open the tomb because they

_____ (believe) their ancestors _____ (put)a curse on it.

Carter _____ (be) British. The British _____ (occupy)

Egypt for years, and they _____ (take) many artifacts back to England.

He _____ (go) ahead and opened the tomb.

Lesson 8
Future Perfect Tense

The future perfect tense expresses action or existence which will be completed in the future.

Learn It

Read these sentences.

By the time the next Olympic Games begin, hundreds of runners *will have* carried this torch.

The runners *will have* trained for at least a year before they carry the torch.

Before the next Olympiad, an Olympic athlete *will have* trained thousands of hours.

Use the future perfect tense to show that an action will be completed by a specified time in the future. It shows that an action will be completed by the time something else happens. To form the future perfect tense, add *shall have* or *will have* to a past participle.

Find It

Underline the verbs in the future perfect tense.

The summer Olympics will be held again in 2008. By the time the Olympic officials meet to decide the location, the United States will have served as host four times. Olympic athletes will have traveled to Greece three times since the modern Olympic Games began there in 1896. Australia will have been a summer Olympic Games site three times too. London, England, will have hosted the games twice. Paris, France, will also have welcomed Olympic athletes two times. The Olympic Committee must decide several years before the event where the Games will be held so the chosen city will have had time to prepare the necessary stadiums and housing for the athletes and spectators. By 2008, the Committee also will probably have added several new sports.

1. Write two sentences using the future perfect tense.

_____

_____

_____

_____

2. Write three sentences using the verb *go*. Write the first sentence using the present perfect tense. Write the second sentence using the past perfect tense. Write the third sentence using the future perfect tense.

_____

_____

_____

_____

_____

_____

_____

_____

Fix It

Fill in the blanks with the future perfect tense of the verb in parentheses.

By next week, Tony _____ his application. (mail)

In two months, he _____ a reply. (receive)

Tony runs for two hours every day. In a week he _____ fourteen hours. (run)

By the time Tony tries out for the Olympics, he _____ a much better runner. (become)

If Tony is not picked for the Olympics, at least he _____ his health. (improve)

Lesson 9

Writing with Perfect Tenses

Using perfect tenses can improve your writing.

Read this paragraph.

> China built the Great Wall to keep out nomads from the North and West. By the time it was completed, the nomads had overrun most of China. The wall runs for almost 1500 miles across northern China to the Yellow Sea. Before the Ming Dynasty, some parts were only high earth mounds. The emperors of China conscripted laborers from all over China to build the wall. Before its completion many had died on the job. The Chinese now want to attract more tourists, so they have reconstructed parts of the wall. By the next decade, thousands of tourists will have visited this famous landmark.

The perfect tenses show the relationship between the times of different actions.

Circle all verbs in any of the perfect tenses.

> The Great Wall of China stretches for thousands of miles. Astronauts have observed it from space. Its average height is 20 feet. A path on the top is 15 feet wide. Parts of the wall date back to 400 BC. An emperor of the Qin (Ch'in) Dynasty connected the existing parts. By the time that dynasty had ended in 206 BC the length of the wall had reached 1,200 miles. The Ming Dynasty ruled from 1368 to 1644. Historians have credited them with finishing the wall. By the end of this year, thousands of tourists will have visited the Great Wall of China.

Try It

Write a report about an historical event. Use perfect tenses to show the relationship between actions.

_____

_____

_____

_____

_____

_____

_____

_____

_____

_____

Fix It

Fill in the blanks with the appropriate form of the verb in parentheses. They may not all be in perfect tenses.

Genghis Khan _____ a great Mongol leader. (be)

Mongols were the "nomads" north of China. Historians _____ that he was born around 1167 in Russia. (decide)

By the time he was thirteen his tribe _____ him the leader. (make)

Members of the tribe were nomads who _____ their hostile neighbors. (subdue)

By 1206, Genghis Khan _____ almost all of Mongolia. (conquer)

Despite the Great Wall, in 1215 the Mongols _____ the capital of China. (capture)

Extra Practice

Lesson 7 **Lesson 8** **Lesson 9**

It is time to practice what you have learned. You have learned how to form and use the present perfect, past perfect, and future perfect tenses.

1. Circle the verbs in the past perfect tense in these sentences.

Thanks to the efforts of Jean Champollion archaeologists have read thousands of inscriptions in hieroglyphics, which their predecessors had failed to decode.

My nephew had visited Egypt several years ago and had come back with a shirt embroidered with his name in hieroglyphics.

In the 1920s the Germans had wanted to start a transatlantic passenger service using lighter-than-air dirigibles filled with hydrogen. The fiery explosion of their airship *Hindenburg* at Lakehurst, New Jersey, in 1937 had put an end to this idea.

Alan Shepard was the first American to fly in space, but a Russian cosmonaut, Yuri Gagarin, had preceded him by three weeks. No human had flown in space before them.

2. Write three sentences of your own using the past perfect tense.

_____

_____

_____

_____

_____

_____

3. Write four sentences using the future perfect tense.

_____

_____

_____

_____

_____

_____

_____

4. Read the paragraph below. Underline verbs in the present perfect tense. Circle verbs in the past perfect tense. Draw two lines under verbs in the future perfect tense.

Most Americans have been sure since they were in elementary school that aviation had its beginning at Kitty Hawk, North Carolina, on December 17, 1903. In fact, aviation had begun 120 years earlier, when hydrogen filled balloons designed by two brothers named Montgolier had carried passengers in France. Balloons have been used for observation in wars ever since, and have been used for years for research on weather. Even recently people have ridden in baskets suspended from balloons. If the winds have been right, and the countries one must pass over have granted permission, it has been possible to circle the globe in a balloon. However, people had wanted to be able to fly as birds do. They had wanted to travel in the air in any direction. Many scientists and engineers had tried to build airplanes that would do this. All except the Wright brothers had failed. More than 600 million people will have flown in the United States by the end of this year, something that only balloon passengers had done at the beginning of the 20th century. Where do you think you will have flown ten years from now?

5. Change the future perfect verbs in the paragraph above to the simple future tense.

_____   _____

Name _____ Date _____ Class _____

Lesson 10

Review

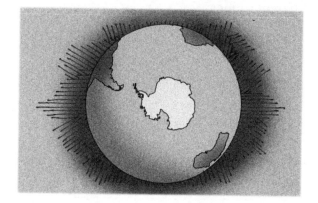

Unit 5

Review It

1. Choose the correct verbs from the box to complete the following sentences.

will have	had lost	have lived

By the time the next Olympic games begin, hundreds of runners _____ carried this torch.

Egyptians used hieroglyphics, a system of figures and objects, to represent ideas and to record

their history, but modern Egyptians _____ the ability to read them.

They _____ there as long as I can remember.

2. Identify the tense of each underlined verb. Write its name in the blank.

My cousin, Sally, wrote me a letter because I <u>had written</u> one to her. _____

After much deliberation, she <u>has decided</u> to go to China. _____

After this trip, she <u>will have visited</u> all the continents but one. _____

I know she will not be happy until she <u>has gone</u> to Antarctica. _____

Sally <u>has wanted</u> me to go with her on several trips. _____

I <u>want</u> to go with her to China. _____

I <u>have read</u> many books about this country. _____

For sure, I <u>want</u> to go to Antarctica. _____

Unit 5 • Lesson 10 • Review **129**

3. Write a short report on something that interests you. Use the perfect tenses to show relationships in time between different actions.

_____

_____

_____

_____

_____

_____

_____

4. Change the base form of the verb in parentheses to the appropriate tense in these sentences.

For centuries the Chinese (seek) a way to keep out invaders.

When it was finished, the construction of the great wall (take) almost two thousand years.

By 1208, Genghis Khan (lead) the Mongols inside the Great Wall of China.

The Mongols invaded Turkey because the Turks (sweep) down and murdered some Mongol traders.

The Turks fled to the west because the Mongols (overrun) their land.

In recent years, tourism in China (rise).

By the end of this summer, thousands of tourists (walk) on the Great Wall of China.

Mary (gain) a new respect for the Chinese people.

In 1920, China (have) a population of an estimated 438 million.

In 1998, the population (be) about 1 billion, 237 million.

I wonder what the population (be) in the year 2010.

Glossary

Abbreviation ♦ **1.** To abbreviate something means to make it shorter. **2.** Some abbreviations begin with a capital letter and end with a period: *Mr. St. Mon.* **3.** When abbreviating a state, use two capital letters and no periods: *CA TX AL*

Action Verb ♦ **1.** An action verb is a verb that shows action. The boy *runs*. **2.** A verb showing what the subject *does* or *has*. The rabbit *ate* the turnips.

Adjective ♦ An adjective tells you more about a noun. The *brown* rabbit ate the turnips.

Adverb ♦ **1.** An adverb tells how, when, or where. **2.** Adverbs can be placed almost anywhere in the sentence. **3.** Adverbs often end in *ly*. Adverbs ending in *ly* are adverbs made from other words like *loud* and *easy*. The rabbit ate the turnips *greedily*. **4.** Adverbs give more information about verbs, adjectives, and other adverbs. He runs *fast*. That is a *very* blue ball. That boy is running *really* fast.

Apostrophe ' ♦ **1.** This ' is an apostrophe. Use an apostrophe to show that something is owned. For singular nouns, write the noun, add the apostrophe, and then add *s*. *Joe's book. Julie's shoes.* For regular plural nouns, write the plural noun and then add the apostrophe. The three *dogs'* bowls were broken. The two *cats'* brushes were lost. **2.** An apostrophe is used to make a contraction. The apostrophe shows that some letters have been left out: *cannot* becomes *can't.*

Article ♦ **1.** The words *a, an,* and *the* are called articles. They help us find nouns. **2.** We use the article *an* with words that begin with a vowel sound. We use the article *a* with words that begin with a consonant sound. We use the article *the* to refer to the noun we are talking about or a plural noun: *a cat, the cat, the cats, an apple, the apples.*

Capitalize ♦ To make a small, or lowercase, letter into a capital, or uppercase, letter is to capitalize.

Comma , ♦ A punctuation mark used between items in a series and before a coordinating conjunction in compound sentences.

Complement ♦ A linking verb links the subject to a complement. A complement completes the predicate. The dog is *happy*. It is a good *pet*.

Complete Predicate ♦ The simple predicate, or verb, and all the words that go with it are called the complete predicate. We *were playing together in the park*.

Glossary

Complete Subject ◆ The simple subject—nouns, pronouns, and gerunds—and all the words that modify it are called the complete subject. *The furry **cat** and the spotted **dog** in the yard* are playing together.

Compound Direct Object ◆ Two or more direct objects that receive the action of a transitive verb are a compound direct object. She gave *the book and the pencil* to him.

Compound Indirect Object ◆ A compound indirect object has two or more indirect objects joined by a conjunction. She gave *Ralph and Oscar* the books.

Compound Predicate ◆ A compound predicate has two or more verbs and two or more predicates connected with a conjunction. The man *ate hot dogs and drank soda.*

Compound Predicate Adjective ◆ Two or more adjectives connected by a conjunction and following a linking verb are a compound predicate adjective. He was *happy* and *proud.*

Compound Predicate Nouns ◆ Two or more nouns connected by a conjunction and following a linking verb are compound predicate nouns. Compound predicate nouns rename or explain a subject. The girls are *Jenny and Sara.*

Compound Sentence ◆ A compound sentence is two complete sentences put together with a coordinating conjunction. *The man ate hot dogs, and his wife ate the french fries.*

Compound Subject ◆ A compound subject is two or more subjects joined with a . . . . conjunction. *The man and woman* ate hot dogs.

Conjunction ◆ A conjunction joins together words or groups of words in a sentence. You can study math *or* science.

Contraction ◆ A contraction is made when one or more words are made shorter by leaving out some letters and replacing them with an apostrophe: *do not* becomes *don't.*

Coordinating Conjunction ◆ Coordinating conjunctions link words, phrases, and clauses of equal importance. The seven coordinating conjunctions are *and, but, so, yet, for, nor,* and *or.* The opossum was awake, *but* the raccoon was asleep.

Correlative Conjunction ◆ Pairs of conjunctions working together to join subjects, predicates, or complete sentences. The most common correlative conjunctions are *neither/nor* and *either/or. Neither* Mary *nor* John will go. *Either* I can use the PC, *or* I can use the Macintosh.

Days of the Week ◆ Capitalize the first letter of the days of the week: *Tuesday*

Declarative Sentence ◆ A declarative sentence tells you about something. *I like ice cream.*

Demonstrative Adjectives ◆ A demonstrative adjective points to something in particular. *This* and *these* point to something close. *That* and *those* point to something farther away.

Demonstrative Pronoun ◆ A pronoun that shows something. *This*, *that*, *these*, and *those* are pronouns that we can use when we are talking about something we are showing. *This* is my book. *That* is Tim's bike.

Direct Object ◆ A transitive verb carries the action from the subject to something or someone else. This something or someone is called a direct object. The direct object can be a noun or a pronoun. She gave the *book* to him.

Exclamation Point ！ ◆ An exclamation point is used at the end of a sentence that shows strong feeling. *That was so much fun!*

Exclamatory Sentence ◆ An exclamatory sentence shows strong feeling. It begins with a capital letter and ends with an exclamation point. *I had a great time!*

Family Members ◆ When you use a word like mom, dad, grandmother, or grandfather as a name, you must use a capital letter. Where are the lunches, *Mom*?

Future Perfect Tense ◆ Use the future perfect tense to show that an action will be completed by the time something else happens. The mail *will have come* by the time I get home.

Gerund ◆ The present participle of a verb used as a noun is called a gerund. He also enjoyed *running*.

Holiday ◆ Capitalize the first letter of each word in the name of a holiday: *St. Patrick's Day.*

I ◆ Always capitalize the word *I*. Carlos and *I* will be studying math together.

Imperative Sentence ◆ An imperative sentence gives an order or command. The subject *you* is understood. *Put your seatbelt on.*

Indent ◆ A paragraph begins with an indent. The indent tells the reader that a new paragraph has started. In compositions, the beginning of a paragraph starts about five spaces in from the left margin.

Interjection ◆ Interjections show the emotion or attitude of the speaker. Use them with commas unless the feeling is very strong. Then, use an exclamation point. Capitalize the first letter of the word after the interjection with an exclamation point. Do not capitalize the first letter of the word after the interjection with a comma.

Indirect Object ◆ An indirect object names a person or thing that indirectly

Glossary

receives the action of the verb. It can come between the verb and the direct object. She gave *him* the book. The President gave *Congress* a speech.

Interrogative Pronoun ◆ Interrogative pronouns introduce questions. The interrogative pronouns are *who*, *whose*, *which*, *what*, and *whom*. *Who* wants candy? *Which* kind of candy do you want? *What* is for dinner?

Interrogative Sentence ◆ An interrogative sentence asks a question. It starts with a capital letter and ends with a question mark. *How are you?*

Intransitive verb ◆ When a verb does not carry any action from the subject to something or someone, it is called an intransitive verb. *The car stopped suddenly.*

Irregular Plural Noun ◆ A noun whose plural form is not created by adding *-s* or *-es* to the singular form is an irregular plural noun. *mouse*, *mice*; *child*, *children*.

Irregular Verb ◆ A verb whose past and past participle forms are not created in the usual way is an irregular verb. *swim, swam swum*; *do, did, done*.

Linking Verb ◆ A verb, mainly the *be* verb, linking the subject to identifying or describing words. The man *is* my father.

Month ◆ Capitalize the first letter of the name of a month: *January*.

Names of Toys or Pets ◆ Capitalize the first letter of the names of toys or pets: *Dino, Barbie*.

Noun ◆ A noun is the name of a person, place, idea, or thing: *boy*, *city*, *table*.

Object of the Preposition ◆ The noun or pronoun in a prepositional phrase is called the object of the preposition. The house on the *corner* is yellow.

Paragraph ◆ A paragraph is how you organize your ideas when you write a composition, such as a story or a report. A paragraph has a topic, which is what the paragraph is about. In compositions, the beginning of a paragraph starts about five spaces from the margin.

Past Perfect Tense ◆ Use the past perfect tense to say that an action was completed by the time another action occurred. Use the verb *had* with the past participle to form past perfect tense. I *had become tired* by noon.

Past Tense ◆ **1.** The past tense of regular verbs is formed by adding *ed* to the verb. **2.** Use the past tense with the past perfect tense to show the relationship between two actions. Yesterday, I *walked* to school. I *had walked* to school only twice before.

People's Names ◆ Capitalize the first letter of a person's name: *Mary*.

Perfect Tense ◆ You make the perfect tense by adding some form of the verb *have* before the past participle form of the verb. Most past participle forms of verbs end in *ed*. There are three perfect tenses: present perfect, past perfect, and future perfect. Perfect tenses show the relationship between the time of different actions. She *has brought* us some information. I *had become tired* by noon. The mail *will have come* by the time I get home.

Phrase ◆ A group of words that forms a unit. It does not have a subject, a verb, or both: *to the store*, *running in a race*, *for her*.

Places ◆ Capitalize the first letter of the names of places: *New York*.

Plural ◆ Plural means more than one: *cats*, *apples*, *cities*, *they*, *them*.

Plural Noun ◆ A noun that names more than one thing: *cats*.

Plural Possessive Adjective ◆ A plural possessive adjective shows that two or more things or people own something. *their* books, *our* classes.

Plural Possessive Noun ◆ A plural possessive noun is a plural noun that shows more than one thing or person owning something: the *bees'* hive.

Possessive ◆ The word *possessive* means that someone or something owns something. *Jack's* boots are very shiny. *My* clothes are new.

Predicate ◆ The word *predicate* can mean two things. Sometimes it means "the verb" only. This is also called a *simple predicate*. Sometimes it means "the verb and all the words that go with it." This is also called a *complete predicate*. *The rabbit **ate the carrots in the garden***. In this sentence, the verb or simple predicate is *ate*. The complete predicate is *ate the carrots in the garden*.

Predicate Adjective ◆ A predicate adjective describes the subject. A linking verb connects the predicate adjective to the subject. The dog is *black*.

Predicate Nominative ◆ A predicate nominative is the same as a predicate noun. A noun that follows a linking verb is a predicate nominative. Predicate nominatives rename or explain a subject. Mr. Downing is the *principal* at my school.

Predicate Noun ◆ Predicate noun is another name for predicate nominative.

Preposition ◆ Prepositions *link* nouns, pronouns, and gerunds to other words. He is a friend *of* mine.

Prepositional Phrase ◆ A preposition followed by a noun, pronoun, or verbal noun is a prepositional phrase. He is a friend *of mine*.

Glossary

Present Participle ◆ The *-ing* form of a verb *roll* + *ing* = *rolling*. A stone was *rolling* down the hill.

Present Perfect Tense ◆ Use the present perfect tense to report an action begun in the past and extending into the present, to report a past action that relates to something in the present, and to report an action completed at some unspecified time in the past. The present perfect tense always uses the present tense of *have* — *have* and *has*. She *has brought* us some information.

Present Tense ◆ The present tense uses the base form of the verb or the base form with an *s*. Greg *takes* the bus to school every day.

Principal Parts of Verbs ◆ The principal parts of verbs are the verb forms from which tenses are formed. Every verb has a present, past, and past participle form. For regular verbs, the past and past participle forms are created by adding *-ed* to the present form. For irregular verbs, the past and past participle forms are created differently.

Present	Past	Past Participle
like	liked	liked
be	was	been
begin	began	begun

Pronoun ◆ Pronouns are words that replace or refer to nouns. *They* are coming to my birthday party. *He* is bringing a present. *They* and *He* are pronouns.

Proper Noun ◆ A proper noun is the special name of a person, a place, or a thing. *Jennifer* is a girl. *Little Rock* is a city. *Lee's Socks* is the name for a special kind of socks.

Question Mark **?** ◆ A question mark is used at the end of a sentence that asks a question. *Will we go skating on Friday?*

Quotation Marks **" "** ◆ Use quotation marks to enclose the exact words someone says. Place the quotation marks at the beginning and end of what a person said.

Reflexive Pronoun ◆ A "self" pronoun showing that the action is reflected upon the doer of the action is a reflexive pronoun.

Regular Verbs ◆ A verb whose past and past participle forms are created by adding *-ed* to the present form is a regular verb: *love, loved, loved*; *seem, seemed, seemed.*

Sentence ◆ A sentence begins with a capital letter. It ends with a mark that shows that the sentence has ended. It is a complete thought that makes sense. *Some birds have beautiful feathers.*

Simple Future Tense ◆ The simple future tense is made with the base form of the verb and *will*. Use the simple future tense to report a future event or state, to indicate willingness or intent to do something, and to indicate probability or expected action. I *will go* with you.

Simple Past Tense ◆ The simple past usually has an *ed* ending except for irregular verbs. Some examples of these are *saw*, *went*, and *ran*. Use the simple past tense to report an action that was completed in the past. It *snowed* yesterday.

Simple Present Tense ◆ The simple present tense is usually the base form of a regular verb. Use the simple present tense when talking or writing about something that happens regularly or is happening now. It *is snowing*.

Simple Subject ◆ The nouns or pronouns that are the subjects of the sentences are simple subjects. The simple subject does *not* include any other words— such as adjectives and prepositional phrases—that modify it. Twenty-five adult *cats* were in the shelter.

Singular ◆ Singular means one: *cat*, *apple*, *city*, *he*, *she*, *it*.

Singular Noun ◆ A noun that names just one thing is called a singular noun: *book*, *cat*, *table*.

Subject ◆ The word *subject* can mean two things. Sometimes it means "the noun or the pronoun" only that is the subject of the sentence. This is also called a simple subject. Sometimes it means "the noun or pronoun that is the subject of the verb and all the words that go with it." This is also called a *complete subject*. *The fluffy, white, billowing clouds on the horizon* reminded them of cotton candy. In this sentence, the simple subject is *clouds*. The complete subject is *The fluffy, white, billowing clouds on the horizon*.

Subject-Verb Agreement ◆ When the subject is plural, the verb must be plural. When the subject is singular, the verb must be singular. We call this subject-verb agreement. The verb always agrees with the subject in number. The *rabbit eats* carrots. The *rabbits eat* carrots.

Tense ◆ The word *tense* means the time that an action happened. The tenses are present, past, and future. Present tense — Everyday I *brush* my teeth. Past tense — Yesterday I *brushed* my teeth. Future tense — Tomorrow I *will brush* my teeth.

Title ◆ A title is a word that is attached to a person's name. A title tells something about the person. Capitalize the first letter in a title: *Dr. Smith*. The titles of published works, movies, TV shows, and musical compositions should be underlined or italicized. I cried after seeing *Titanic*.

Transitive Verb ◆ When the verb carries the action from the subject to something or someone, it is called a transitive verb. *He gave the book to her.*

Glossary

Topic Sentence ◆ Every paragraph has a topic—what the paragraph is about. Often, that topic is stated in a topic sentence, such as *The bandicoot is a misunderstood animal* or *Year-round schooling is not a good idea*. The other sentences in the paragraph give more information about the topic sentence. These are called supporting details. A topic sentence may appear at the beginning, the middle, or at the end of a paragraph.

Verb ◆ A verb is a word that shows action (*dive, shout, cry*) or existence (*are, is, was*).

Verb Forms ◆ present form: *roll*, present participle: *rolling = roll + ing*, past participle: *rolled = roll + ed*.

Verbal ◆ A verbal is a present or past participle. It is used as a noun or an adjective. We saw the *rolling* hills of Ohio. *Fishing* is my hobby.

Verbal Adjective ◆ A participle used as an adjective can be called a verbal adjective, because it comes from a verb. The *snoring* cat is sleeping. Jim has a *broken* arm.

Verbal Noun ◆ The present participle of a verb used as a noun is called a verbal noun. Some books call these *gerunds*. A verbal noun can have many parts of speech after it. *Watching* the commercial made me thirsty.

Charts

Personal Pronouns

Person	Singular	Plural
First	I	we
Second	you	you
Third	he, she, it	they

Used in place of nouns.

Possessive Pronouns

Person	Singular	Plural
First	my	ours
Second	yours	yours
Third	his, hers, its	theirs

Used to show ownership.

Demonstrative Pronouns

	Singular	Plural
Things Near	this	these
Things Farther Away	that	those

Used to show someone or something.

Interrogative Pronouns

what
which
who
whom
whose

Used to introduce questions.

Charts

Measurement Abbreviations

Measurement	Abbreviation
centimeter	cm
cubic foot	cu. ft.
cubic inch	cu. in.
cubic yard	cu. yd.
cup	c.
fluid ounce	fl. oz.
foot	ft.
gallon	gal.
gram	g
hour	hr.
inch	in.
kilogram	kg
kiloliter	kl
kilometer	km
liter	l
meter	m
metric ton	t
mile	mi.
millimeter	mm
minute	min.
month	mo.
ounce	oz.
pint	pt.
pound	lb.
quart	qt.
second	sec.
square foot	sq. ft.
square inch	sq. in.
square yard	sq. yd.
tablespoon	Tbsp.
teaspoon	tsp.
ton	T.
week	wk.
yard	yd.
year	yr.

Title Abbreviations

To indicate a(n)	Use
doctor	Dr.
senator	Sen.
married woman	Mrs.
a married or unmarried woman, depending on personal preference	Ms.
any man	Mr.
Reverend	Rev.

Calendar Abbreviations

Month	Abbreviation
January	Jan.
February	Feb.
March	Mar.
April	Apr.
May	May
June	June
July	July
August	Aug.
September	Sept.
October	Oct.
November	Nov.
December	Dec.

Day	Abbreviation
Sunday	Sun.
Monday	Mon.
Tuesday	Tues.
Wednesday	Wed.
Thursday	Thurs.
Friday	Fri.
Saturday	Sat.

State Abbreviations

State	Abbreviation
Alabama	AL
Alaska	AK
Arizona	AZ
Arkansas	AR
California	CA
Colorado	CO
Connecticut	CT
Delaware	DE
District of Columbia	DC
Florida	FL
Georgia	GA
Hawaii	HI
Idaho	ID
Illinois	IL
Indiana	IN
Iowa	IA
Kansas	KS
Kentucky	KY
Louisiana	LA
Maine	ME
Maryland	MD
Massachusetts	MA
Michigan	MI
Minnesota	MN
Mississippi	MS
Missouri	MO
Montana	MT
Nebraska	NE
Nevada	NV
New Hampshire	NH
New Jersey	NJ
New Mexico	NM
New York	NY

State Abbreviations

State	Abbreviation
North Carolina	NC
North Dakota	ND
Ohio	OH
Oklahoma	OK
Oregon	OR
Pennsylvania	PA
Rhode Island	RI
South Carolina	SC
South Dakota	SD
Tennessee	TN
Texas	TX
Utah	UT
Vermont	VT
Virginia	VA
Washington	WA
West Virginia	WV
Wisconsin	WI
Wyoming	WY

State abbreviations don't have periods.

Address Abbreviations

Address	Abbreviation
Avenue	Ave.
Boulevard	Blvd.
Post Office	PO
Road	Rd.
Street	St.
Suite	Ste.

Charts

Contractions

are not . . . . aren't
cannot . . . . can't
could not . . . . couldn't
has not . . . . hasn't
have not . . . . haven't
he has . . . . he's
he is . . . . he's
he will . . . . he'll
I am . . . . I'm
I have . . . . I've
I will . . . . I'll
is not . . . . isn't
it has . . . . it's
it is . . . . it's
it will . . . . it'll
might not . . . . mightn't
never . . . . ne'er
over . . . . o'er
she has . . . . she's
she is . . . . she's
she will . . . . she'll
should not . . . . shouldn't
they are . . . . they're
they have . . . . they've
they will . . . . they'll
was not . . . . wasn't
we have . . . . we've
we will . . . . we'll
were not . . . . weren't
will not . . . . won't
you are . . . . you're
you have . . . . you've
you will . . . . you'll

You make a contraction by leaving out some letters and replacing them with an apostrophe.

Adverbs

Where	When	How
above	again and	almost
away	again	completely
backward	already	deeply
below	always	enough
downstairs	before	exactly
far	daily	greatly
forward	first	highly
here	immediately	just
near	never	nearly
there	next	really
upstairs	now	somewhat
where	once	too
	sometime	very
	soon	widely
	still	wrongly
	then	
	today	
	tomorrow	
	twice	
	yesterday	

Making Nouns into Adjectives

Noun	to	Adjective
able	. . . .	ably
act	. . . .	active
beauty	. . . .	beautiful
care	. . . .	careful
fad	. . . .	faddish
fear	. . . .	fearful
gloom	. . . .	gloomy
glory	. . . .	glorious
hair	. . . .	hairy
hand	. . . .	handily
ice	. . . .	icy
job	. . . .	jobless
kink	. . . .	kinky
lump	. . . .	lumpy
magic	. . . .	magical
noise	. . . .	noisy
orbit	. . . .	orbital
play	. . . .	playful
skill	. . . .	skillful
taste	. . . .	tasteful
wonder	. . . .	wonderful

You can make adjectives from nouns by adding different endings.

Possessive Adjectives

Person	Singular	Plural
First	my	our
Second	your	your
Third	his, her, its	their

Charts

Making Adjectives into Adverbs

Adjective	Adverb
active	actively
beautiful	beautifully
careful	carefully
dainty	daintily
fair	fairly
gay	gaily
great	greatly
happy	happily
hungry	hungrily
immediate	immediately
jealous	jealously
large	largely
lazy	lazily
magical	magically
noisy	noisily
odd	oddly
pretty	prettily
rapid	rapidly
skillful	skillfully
slow	slowly
swift	swiftly
tasteful	tastefully
wonderful	wonderfully

You can make adverbs from adjectives by adding *ly*.

Coordinating Conjunctions

Coordinating Conjunction	Meaning
and	add, put together
but, yet	opposites & exceptions
for	because
nor	negative choice for both
or	choice, but not both
so	what follows from the first action

Used to join complete sentences.

Correlative Conjunctions

both . . . . . . .and	not only . . . . .but also
either . . . . . .or	not . . . . .nor
neither . . . . .nor	never . . . . . . .nor

After *nor*, reverse the subject and verb.

Prepositions

aboard	behind	from	throughout
about	below	in	to
above	beneath	into	toward
across	beside	like	towards
after	besides	near	under
against	between	of	underneath
along	beyond	off	until
amid	but	on	unto
amidst	by	onto	up
among	concerning	out	upon
around	down	over	with
as	during	past	within
at	except	since	without
before	for	through	

Most Common Prepositions

almost	for	of
at	from	on
by	in	to

Charts

Irregular Verbs

Present Tense	Past Tense

Irregular Verbs

Present Tense	Past Tense
am/is	was
awake/awakes	awoke
become/becomes	became
bite/bites	bit
bring/brings	brought
buy/buys	bought
catch/catches	caught
choose/chooses	chose
cut/cuts	cut
come/comes	came
creep/creeps	crept
deal/deals	dealt
do/does	did
dream/dreams	dreamt or dreamed
drink/drinks	drank
eat/eats	ate
fall/falls	fell
feel/feels	felt
forget/forgets	forgot
get/gets	got
give/gives	gave
go/goes	went
grow/grows	grew
have/has	had
hear/hears	heard
hit/hits	hit
hold/holds	held
keep/keeps	kept
know/knows	knew
lay/lays	laid
lead/leads	led
leap/leaps	leapt
lie/lies	lay
light/lights	lit or lighted

Present Tense	Past Tense
lose/loses	lost
make/makes	made
meet/meets	met
pay/pays	paid
put/puts	put
read/reads	read
rid/rids	rid or ridded
ride/rides	rode
ring/rings	rang
run/runs	ran
say/says	said
see/sees	saw
seek/seeks	sought
sell/sells	sold
sing/sings	sang
sit/sits	sat
sleep/sleeps	slept
slide/slides	slid
smell/smells	smelt or smelled
speak/speaks	spoke
spring/springs	sprang or sprung
sting/stings	stung
stink/stinks	stank or stunk
sweep/sweeps	swept
swim/swims	swam
swing/swings	swung
take/takes	took
teach/teaches	taught
tell/tells	told
think/thinks	thought
wake/wakes	woke
was	were
weep/weeps	wept
write/writes	wrote

Irregular Verbs

Base Form	Past Tense	Past Participle
arise	arose	arisen
awake	awoke	awaked
be	was, were	been
bear	bore	borne, born
begin	began	begun
bend	bent	bent
bid	bade, bid	bidden, bid
bind	bound	bound
bite	bit	bitten
bleed	bled	bled
blow	blew	blown
break	broke	broken
breed	bred	bred
bring	brought	brought
burst	burst	burst
buy	bought	bought
cast	cast	cast
catch	caught	caught
choose	chose	chosen
cling	clung	clung
come	came	come
cost	cost	cost
creep	crept	crept
cut	cut	cut
deal	dealt	dealt
dig	dug	dug
do	did	done
draw	drew	drawn
drink	drank	drunk
drive	drove	driven
eat	ate	eaten
fall	fell	fallen
feed	fed	fed
feel	felt	felt

Irregular Verbs

Base Form	Past Tense	Past Participle
fight	fought	fought
find	found	found
flee	fled	fled
fling	flung	flung
fly	flew	flown
forget	forgot	forgotten
forgive	forgave	forgiven
freeze	frooze	frozen
get	got	gotten
give	gave	given
go	went	gone
grow	grew	grown
hang	hung, hanged	hung, hanged
have	had	had
hear	heard	heard
hide	hid	hidden
hold	held	held
keep	kept	kept
kneel	knelt	knelt
know	knew	known
lead	led	led
leave	left	left
lend	lent	lent
lie	lay	lain
light	lit, lighted	lit, lighted
lose	lost	lost
make	made	made
mean	meant	meant
put	put	put
read	read	read
ride	rode	ridden
ring	rang	rung
rise	rose	risen
say	said	said

Charts

Irregular Verbs

Base Form	Past Tense	Past Participle
see	saw	seen
sell	sold	sold
send	sent	sent
set	set	set
shake	shook	shaken
shine	shone, shined	shone, shined
shoot	shot	shot
shrink	shrank, shrunk	shrunk, shrunken
sing	sang	sung
sink	sank	sunk, sunken
sit	sat	sat
sleep	slept	lept
speak	spoke	spoken
spend	spent	spent
spin	spun	spun
spit	spat	spat
spread	spread	spread
spring	sprang, sprung	sprung
stand	stood	stood
steal	stole	stolen
stick	stuck	stuck
sting	stunk, stank	stunk
strike	struck	struck, stricken
string	strung	strung
sweep	swept	swept
swim	swam, swum	swum
swing	swung, swang	swung
take	took	taken
teach	taught	taught
tear	tore	torn
think	thought	thought
wake	woke, waked	waked, woken
wear	wore	worn

Past Participles for Some Regular Verbs

Base Form	Past Participle
bathe	bathed
button	buttoned
clothe	clothed
collect	collected
dry	dried
heat	heated
mend	mended
prepare	prepared
scare	scared
smoke	smoked
sweat	sweated

Add *ed* to the bare form. Sometimes *y* goes to *i*.

Past Participles for Some Irregular Verbs

Base Form	Past Participle
break	broken
cut	cut
drink	drunk
eat	eaten
know	known
lend	lent
light	lit
pay	paid
rot	rotten
sew	sewn
speak	spoken
tear	torn
write	written

Make spelling changes or no change.

Student Notes

Student Notes